Contents

Acknowledgements

We would like to thank these publishers and authors for granting permission to reprint extracts from the following works:

Jonathan Cape Ltd for 'I Like that Stuff' by Adrian Mitchell

Edward Arnold (Publishers) Ltd for *Howards End* by E.M. Forster

W.H. Allen & Co. Ltd for *Saturday Night and Sunday Morning* by Alan Sillitoe

Jonathan Cape Ltd and the Executors of the James Joyce Estate for extracts from *Dubliners* and *A Portrait of the Artist as a Young Man*

Centerprise Trust Ltd for 'Embroidery' by Emily Bishop from *Working Lives*; 'Willy the Watchmender' extract by Ron Barnes from Hackney Writers' Workshop, Vol. 1; 'Terrace', by Sue Shrapnel, from Hackney Writers' Workshop Vol. 3; 'By Omission' by Les Skeates from Hackney Writers' Workshop Vol. 3

A.D. Peters and Co. Ltd for 'Spiv in Love' from *Late Night in Watling Street* by Bill Naughton

Harold Ober Associates Inc. for 'You Should Have Seen the Mess' from *The Go-Away Bird and other stories* by Muriel Spark, Copyright © 1958

Jonathan Cape Ltd and the Executors of the Ernest Hemingway Estate for 'Hills Like White Elephants' and 'Soldier's Home' from *The First Forty-Nine Stories* and in Canada, Charles Scribner's Sons for 'Hills Like White Elephants' from *The Short Stories of Ernest Hemingway*, © copyright 1927 Charles Scribner's Sons, © copyright renewed 1955 Ernest Hemingway: and also for 'Soldier's Home' from *In Our Time*, © copyright 1925 Charles Scribner's Sons, © copyright renewed 1953 Ernest Hemingway

Ian McEwan for extracts from 'In Between the Sheets' and 'Psychopolis' from *In Between the Sheets*

Penguin Books Ltd for 'The Disinterested Killer Bill Harrigan' by Jorge Luis Borges, from *A Universal History of Infamy* (Penguin Books 1975), pp. 63-65, Copyright © Emecé Editores S.A. and Norman Thomas di Giovanni, 1970, 1971, 1972; 'Notes from Underground', translated by Jessie Coulson (Penguin Classics 1972) Copyright © Jessie Coulson, 1972; for adaptation from *Do you Love Me?* by R.D. Laing (Penguin Books 1977) p. 25, Copyright © R.D. Laing

Actac (Theatrical and Cinematic) Ltd for *Out of the Flying Pan* by David Campton Copyright © 1961 David Campton

Michael B. Yeats, Anne Yeats and Macmillan London, Ltd for lines from 'Under Ben Bulben's Head' by W.B. Yeats

Hodder and Stoughton Ltd. for 'Catalogue' from *Does it Have to Rhyme* by Sandy Brownjohn

Warner Bros Inc and Bob Dylan for extract from 'A Hard Rain's A-Gonna Fall' by Bob Dylan: © 1963 Warner Bros Inc, All Rights Reserved

The author also wishes to acknowledge with thanks the help of the following:

David Elliot, Judith Graham, Judith Holden, Saleem Peeradina, Chris Taylor, and the following, whose work appears in this book:

Sarah Gillam, Kamal, Darrol Kenworthy, Deepak Manchanda, Dipti Mehta, Fareeda Mehta, Pheruzi, Dipti Shah, Salil Tripathi.

How to use this book

This book is designed to help you learn about imaginative, or creative, writing. You cannot be taught how to write, but you can learn about it, as every writer however great or famous has had to learn about it — through writing, through criticism of their writing, through reading, through watching and thinking. The teaching of creative writing in schools, the development of writers' groups, evening classes and community publishers has given an enormous number of people the encouragement to write for their own pleasure and stimulation. The notion of a writer as somebody unique, with a special education and a private income is no longer valid — if it ever was. All that is needed is a willingness to experiment, to develop critical powers, to read what other people have written — and to write.

Don't worry for the moment about publication and fame. The number of people who make a living from their imaginative writing has always been tiny, and big publishers generally take on only a small amount of new fiction. There are a number of different ways in which you can make your writing available other than by having it commercially published. It could mean publication by a community press, a local bookshop or one of what are called the 'little presses'. Or it could mean your reproducing a small number of copies with one of the many reprographic methods now available, such as photocopying, duplicating, or printing on a small offset litho machine.

This book is a practical guide to developing different imaginative writing skills. It covers the established forms of fiction and poetry and the questions which frequently occur when considering them — what kinds of things you should feel confident in writing about, what makes good dialogue, the use of settings, who should tell the story, how to start writing poems or drama, and so on. But it also emphasises the possibilities offered by writing of an experimental nature, looking here at both unpublished and published work. Unusual kinds of short story, poem or drama are discussed, as well as some pieces which don't fit easily into any of these categories. The emphasis throughout is on the small scale, that which is manageable in a limited period of time, rather than on the demands of writing, say, full-length novels.

The final synthesis, the putting together of the different elements discussed in the course of the book, in a poem or story or play, is up to you. No guide can teach you that — you learn about it by doing it. What this book offers you is a wide range of different ways in to imaginative writing, which is why nearly all chapters are followed by a substantial list of ideas for writing. It isn't essential to read the chapters in order, as they do stand on their own, but reference is sometimes made to previous chapters.

The first section of the book concentrates mostly on prose writing, a medium which comes more naturally to many people than poetry, though many of the ideas are also applicable to poetry.

'Where to start' suggests that it is useful to bear a couple of things in mind. One is that good writing is generally concrete rather than abstract, is about situations rather than theories. The other is that your own experience is certainly wide enough for you to be able to write interestingly — no need to wander off what you know.

'Finding a voice' is about writing monologues, in which you create a character who interests you and who talks for a few pages, and becomes familiar to the reader. It's entertaining to do, and you don't have to worry too much about style or plot — the narrator's personality takes care of most of that.

'Time to talk' looks at dialogue, and tries to sort out what it is that makes some dialogue both convincing and interesting and some unbelievable and dull. It also looks at how dialogue and description can enhance each other.

'Writing about people' continues this exploration. There are ways of making a character interesting and alive other than straightforwardly describing him or her. The question is, what is the character's function and role in the story?

'Doing things with places': the same question applies to places in fiction. Are they designed to provide atmosphere, tell us about somebody, suggest a whole way of life, stand for something in a symbolic way? All these possibilities and more are looked at, with examples.

'Who's telling the story?' is an analysis of narrative techniques — first person (the 'I' mode), third person (the 'he/she' mode), and the third person where the focus is on one character. There are advantages and disadvantages with each one, and examples are given.

'Who's telling the story? — second time around' looks at a student's short story in the making, from the first to the final draft, and the thinking in between. The story itself tinkers with the question of who is telling the story.

'The world from the inside' contains examples of very private, experimental pieces which try to get over the feeling of the individual's inner world.

'A proper story' takes a comprehensive look at different kinds of complete short story (those with 'a beginning, a middle and an end')and how you might try writing some of your own. It also includes a reading list of 19th and 20th century short story writers.

The next four sections look at poetry, what it is and how to go about writing it, concentrating again on the small-scale and manageable.

'What is a poem?' tries to give a constructive answer to exactly that question, the intention being to make writing poems (and reading other people's) less daunting and more appealing.

'Just a few lines' continues along this path, suggesting ways of writing short poems which should give some satisfaction and strengthen confidence.

'Ideas into shape' looks at how your ideas can be arranged or 'structured' in a poem in such a way that the poem will take on a clearer shape or 'personality'.

'New worlds, new forms' includes examples of experimental writing (and suggestions for your own) which respond directly to the developments of the modern world — computer poems, futuristic language, consumer's reports, civil defence 'manuals', and so on.

Finally 'A bit of drama': less a guide to how to write conventional plays than a survey of the kinds of situations which make good drama, whether of five minutes' or two hours' duration, and of some different kinds of dialogue.

3

1 Where to start

This opening chapter is concerned with making two broad assertions about imaginative writing. The first is that good imaginative writing is *rooted in the particular*, in particular things, particular people, particular situations, rather than in generalised notions about them. The second, related to this, is that interesting imaginative writing can, and indeed should be, written entirely *from what you know*. Just what it is that you 'know', of course, is a slippery question. What you *don't* know is perhaps easier to judge. While these two assertions are intended to act in some ways as a check, on earnest philosophising on one hand, and on ignorant imitation on the other, they can also be seen as reminders of the possibilities and strengths of imaginative writing.

Rooted in the particular

It really doesn't matter if you want to write but feel you have nothing to say. It may even be an advantage. The poet W.H. Auden used to say that if a prospective poet felt he had something important to tell the world there was little hope for him. If, on the other hand, his reasons for wanting to write were something like 'Because I like to hang around words and overhear them talking to one another', then Auden would conclude that he was at least interested in a fundamental part of the writing process and encourage him to go on.

Flannery O'Connor, the American short story writer, makes much the same point. If you are less interested in people and situations, than in what you want to 'say' about them, then you won't end up with a poem or a story but 'a sketch with an essay woven through it, or an essay with a sketch woven through it, or an editorial with a character in it, or a case history with a moral, or some other mongrel thing.' The writer who ambitiously embarks upon, let us say, a novel specifically about the need for society to accept homosexuality, or the spiritually suffocating effects of mass technology on the individual, runs the risk of producing no more than a sermon on his chosen topic, rather than a novel. His characters are less likely to be believable individuals than pasteboard cutouts designed to illustrate particular social attitudes. For example: A is a homosexual. He is sensitive and good. X is the man who hates A because he releases suppressed homosexual desires in him. Y is the girl who hates A because she finds him threatening to her own female sexuality. Z is the man who understands A and is sympathetic towards him. They are in fact Male Machismo, Female Jealousy and Human Understanding respectively (the last no doubt the author in thin disguise). The novel will have a 'dead' feel to it that a reader won't tolerate. A reader needs to see people and feel sensations in a piece of writing, not be presented with ideas dressed up as something else. The ideas can emerge from the situations, not the other way round.

Many writers describe the germs of things they have written as specific scenes or situations, rather than anything they wanted to tell the world. In 1907 Joseph Conrad published *The Secret Agent*, sometimes described as 'a novel about anarchism,' which has become a classic of modern fiction. It is, more accurately, about anarchists, about people who act in a certain way rather than about the merits of their beliefs. Conrad describes the idea for the book as having sprung from a number of trivial and unconnected things, one of which occurred while talking to a friend. Conrad referred to the recent blowing up of an anarchist by his own bomb at Greenwich Observatory. The friend remarked 'Oh, that fellow was half an idiot. His sister committed suicide afterwards.' His words struck Conrad forcibly, and as he says 'illuminated' him without his knowing why. The novel that emerged focused on the activities of a group of anarchists, and the relationship between one of them, his wife, and her idiot brother — who is blown up by a bomb he has been tricked into carrying, causing the suicide of his sister. The dramatic potential of that horrific accident was similarly recognised by Alfred Hitchcock, who turned it into a film. 'Anarchism,' then, is only a thread in the whole fabric of the story.

Creative writing, unlike journalism or sociology or essay writing, is rooted in the senses. It begins with the concrete. The reason isn't hard to see. After all, we experience our daily lives

5

through our senses, and through our emotions. Creative writing attempts to recapture that vitality, the feel of life as it is lived, not how it is thought about when held at arm's length. How it does this, and to what end, is of course the business of the individual writer. We return to a favourite poem or story with enjoyment, because even if the emotions it produces are sad, what we read is in some way alive. What we respond to, with our senses as well as our minds, is a dramatic reconstruction of reality rather than an essay about it.

What this means in practice (and how it can be done with material always close at hand) may become clearer after looking at the two extracts which follow. Both poems look at the common emotion of affection for familiar objects. One is early 20th century, the other is contemporary. As a result, the tone of voice, the use of language, the choice of objects, is very different. Neither poet speaks in generalities about the things he loves, but confines himself to listing the objects themselves. Nevertheless, we are aware at the end of two wholly different ways of looking at the world.

The first is Rupert Brooke, writing at the turn of the century.

> These I have loved:
> White plates and cups, clean-gleaming,
> Ring'd with blue lines; and feathery, faery dust;
> Wet roofs, beneath the lamp-light; the strong crust
> Of friendly bread; and many-tasting food;
> Rainbows; and the blue bitter smoke of wood;
> And radiant raindrops couching in cool flowers;
> And flowers themselves, that sway through sunny hours,
> Dreaming of moths that drink them under the moon;
> Then, the cool kindliness of sheets, that soon
> Smooth away trouble; and the rough male kiss
> Of blankets; grainy wood; live hair that is
> Shining and free; blue-massing clouds; the keen
> Unpassioned beauty of a great machine;
> The benison of hot water; furs to touch;
> The good smell of old clothes; and others such —
> The comfortable smell of friendly fingers,
> Hair's fragrance, and the musty reek that lingers
> About dead leaves and last year's ferns

> from 'The Great Lover'

Perhaps you can't stand 'white plates and cups . . . ring'd with blue lines'. Tastes change. But there will always be something fresh and vigorous about 'the rough male kiss of blankets'. The comparison gives us an impression of sharply felt, first-hand experience. This is there, too, in the more conventional 'cool kindliness of sheets, that soon smooth away trouble'. There is emotion in the poem, in words like 'friendly', 'kindliness', 'benison', 'comfortable', but what *convinces* us of the friendliness of the bread is its strong crust; we are helped to *feel* the kindliness of the sheets because they are cool. The emotion of the poem reaches us most powerfully at the level of our senses, so that we aren't merely told about these qualities, we feel them in the images (the 'word-pictures') of the poem.

Turning to the language of the poem, though, we immediately run up against a complication. Look at these lines:

> And radiant raindrops couching in cool flowers;
> And flowers themselves, that sway through sunny hours
> Dreaming of moths that drink them under the moon;

Isn't this a bit much, a bit self-consciously 'poetic'? It's dreamy and moony and about flowers so it *looks* like poetry. But do we look at things with a fresh eye after reading this, in the way that we might do after reading 'the rough male kiss of blankets?' No. Because we've heard this kind of thing before. It sounds pretty, but it's second-hand. The tearful lover with pearls on her pillow and all that, pretty-pretty but just not real. For images to work successfully, the language needs to be fresh, so that it seems we are looking at something for the first time.

Here is another, very different, poem about loved objects;

Lovers lie around in it,
Broken glass is found in it.
Grass.
I like that stuff.

Tuna fish get trapped in it.
Legs come wrapped in it.
Nylon.
I like that stuff.

Eskimos and tramps chew it.
Madame Tussaud gave status to it.
Wax.
I like that stuff.

from 'I Like That Stuff'
by Adrian Mitchell

Clearly somebody very different from Rupert Brooke is talking. There is nothing dreamy about Mitchell's poem — by comparison, Brooke appears as a very conventional, romantic young poet. Brooke chooses objects conventionally accepted as beautiful, delicate .... the mood is one of tenderness, submission, at times almost swooning. His poem even hints at a need on his part for love and reassurance. Mitchell's couldn't be more different. Deliberately choosing materials of an 'unpoetic' or homely nature, he offers a lively appraisal of their varied functions. He takes delight in raking up the most disparate forms or uses his 'stuff' can be put to, and pairing them together — fish and women's legs, eskimos and Madame Tussaud's. Don't we mentally go 'ouch' at the lines:

> Lovers lie around in it
> Broken glass is found in it
> Grass

It wouldn't be pretentious to say that both poems are 'about love' — a particular kind of love, as understood by two very different people. But any ideas about love which the poems generate are sparked off by the particular concrete images of the poems. They are about particular things first, about love second. In the same way, Conrad's novel is about anarchists first, particular individuals in particular situations, and about anarchism second.

It would, of course, be absurd to claim that this effect is universal in imaginative writing. Many successful writers are greatly given to generalising and philosophising, much avant-garde art is specifically concerned with exploring ideas rather than particular situations. Nevertheless, these are more exceptions than the rule, and to begin with at least, it might be useful to forget about thinking about ideas in favour of looking at and writing about things — in your own poem about loved objects, for example. It's bound to be different from Brooke's or Mitchell's, just as your way of looking at the world is different.

What you know

The second assertion about imaginative writing, that you should write from what you know, looks simple enough. But this is not the same as to say that what you write must be true and must have happened directly to you. That would be to confine you to autobiography. There are whole areas which we may not know at first hand but of which we feel we have sufficient intuitive knowledge to write about. A son coming home from war, for instance. Might not a writer who has never experienced war himself be able to write a good short story on this subject? The proof could lie only in the reading of the story itself, in the writer's ability to convince us of the people and the emotions in his story, of exhausted relief, of ecstasy, or (as in Hemingway's 'Soldier's Home', quoted on p.46) of disillusionment and apathy.

Perhaps the most fruitful question to ask is 'do I need to wander out of my own experience?' Your own experience may seem narrow to you, an ordinary family in an average town, a few years at the local school and college, a not unusual job. But all the material is there, even if you want to keep to realistic fiction or drama, ignoring the more purely 'imaginative' world of poetry or experimental prose. According to Flannery O'Conner 'anyone who has survived an average childhood has enough to write about for a dozen years.' That this depends on how you see that childhood, and what you make of it, is implied by her use of the word 'survived'. And the same is true of subsequent periods of your life.

It is characteristic of new writers that they should feel limited by their experience. Partly, this is a result of an uncertain understanding of the writing process, which is as much concerned with transformation of experience as with mere description. But it is also a result of the myths that have grown up around some of the great figures of modern literature. A noted example is the American writer Ernest Hemingway, who believed passionately in the value of violent and intense experience. He made his life revolve around war, big game hunting, deep sea fishing, bullfighting and drinking. This was not only intense living, it was desperate living. Finally the despair overtook him and he shot himself. James Joyce was an expatriate, Kafka died of consumption, D.H. Lawrence lived in Mexico . . . and with somebody else's wife. But Joyce and

Lawrence began their lives as schoolteachers, and much of Lawrence's finest writing is based upon the world that he grew up in, the Nottingham mining community. Of Joyce's two most widely read books, *A Portrait of the Artist as a Young Man* and *Dubliners*, the first is almost straight autobiography, the second is a series of sketches of the city he both loved and hated. It's extremely easy to have romantic ideas about unfamiliar places and people, and very tempting to write about them. And it seems to come so easily! It comes so easily, of course, because you're using somebody else's language and material and probably style, and to begin with at least, it's much harder to find your own.

And that's the trouble with the 'exotic' setting. It distracts the writer from the meat of the story, towards the trimmings. In this way it can disguise the true value of the story itself, or the lack of value. Needless to say, this is as true of readers as of writers. It's no accident that a leading publisher of romantic fiction publicises its novels by drawing attention to their settings — love flourishes in tropical islands, historic castles, even (it adds) in the busy atmosphere of a modern hospital. A quick glance at their manufactured plots and cardboard people, and you can see one reason at least why the emphasis is on the setting.

I was once given thirty pages of closely typed manuscript by a foreign student who, it turned out, had once spent a week in Britain. His story was set in England, and turned out to be a threading together of fish and chips, pints of bitter, cream teas, joints of beef, pubs, Stratford-upon-Avon, the river Thames, Trafalgar Square and *Match of the Day*, culminating in a round-Britain cycle race in which the young hero and heroine managed to cycle from Oxford to Liverpool in under two hours. There was obviously a great deal of affection for Britain in his writing, but the results were unfortunate.

'Different from us'

It isn't only beginning writers who fall into this trap, nor is it only romantic settings that lure them, but unfamiliar or inaccessible people and social classes too. Scott Fitzgerald once said in a significant tone of voice to Hemingway: 'The very rich are different from us.' 'Yes,' said Hemingway flatly, 'they have more money.' In our own age, a writer is likely to feel scruples about the social sweep of his fiction. Does it adequately represent the reality of life in a democratic, industrial, multi-racial, pluralist (etc.) society? While these are perhaps important questions to ask, the answer is not necessarily to flesh out your writing to include feminists, merchant bankers, occultists, rock stars, conservationists, oil sheikhs, trade unionists and so on if you happen never to have encountered one of these. You'll probably end up writing an ill-informed essay, not even an ill-informed novel, either because you feel you know it all, or because you don't and feel guilty, and try to hide your ignorance.

A great novelist who strays into a minefield when he moves away from what he knows is E.M. Forster in *Howards End*. In the novel he tries to show, among other things, the divide between social classes and how this might be bridged. He is clearly concerned about this, no doubt also guilty about coming from the privileged upper class which the novel knows and satirises so well. So it becomes necessary to include a character from — The Working Classes! He has one tentative stab. Here it is. Leonard Bast, an insurance clerk, is sitting reading, and painfully 'improving himself', in his basement flat. Jacky, who lives with him, clatters down the stairs.

'What ho!' said Leonard, greeting the apparition with much spirit and helping it off with its boa.
Jacky, in husky tones, replied, 'What ho!'
'Been out?' he asked. The question sounds superfluous, but it cannot have been really, for she answered, 'No,' adding, 'Oh, I am so tired.'
'You tired?'
'Eh?'
'I'm tired,' said he, hanging the boa up.
'Oh, Len, I am so tired.'
'I've been to that classical concert I told you about,' said Leonard.
'What's that?'
'I came back as soon as it was over.'
'Anyone been round to our place?' asked Jacky.
'Not that I've seen. I met Mr Cunningham outside, and we passed a few remarks.'
'What, not Mr Cunningham?'
'Yes. Mr Cunningham.'
'I've been out to tea at a lady friend's.'

Her secret being at last given to the world, and the name
of the lady friend being even adumbrated, Jacky made no
further experiments in the difficult and tiring art of
conversation. She never had been a great talker. Even in
her photographic days she had relied upon her smile and
her figure to attract, and now that she was —

On the shelf,
On the shelf,
Boys, boys, I'm on the shelf,

she was not likely to find her tongue. Occasional bursts of
song (of which the above is an example) still issued from
her lips, but the spoken word was rare.

She sat down on Leonard's knee, and began to fondle
him. She was now a massive woman of thirty-three, and her
weight hurt him, but he could not very well say anything.
Then she said, 'Is that a book you're reading?' and he said
'That's a book,' and drew it from her unreluctant grasp.

There's everything wrong with this. It's unbelievable (the
irrelevant, absurd 'Mr Cunningham' business), it's superior (the
opening description of Jacky), it's crude in its humour (Leonard
struggling under her 'massive' weight). And the reason is clear.
Forster doesn't know his subject from inside, and tries to hide it
by turning them into figures of fun. This is a short-term trick,
and springs back in his face when he next lets us meet the Basts
and expects us to believe in them as important characters in the
novel.

Here is another novelist, less highly regarded yet in this case
as always, keeping to what he knows well, the factories, pubs and
terraced streets of Nottingham. The passage is from Alan
Sillitoe's *Saturday Night and Sunday Morning*. Arthur, the
complacent, womanising hero is standing at a bar. A young
woman comes up to buy drinks.

'Have a drink then, duck, while you're here.'
She looked over her shoulder at the others, and, seeing
them still talking, said: 'All right. I'll have a shandy if you
don't mind. What's that black stuff you're drinking? It looks
like treacle.' He told her. 'I've heard of it,' she said. 'I think
I tasted it once, but it was too strong.' She sipped her
shandy. 'This is as much as I can take.'
'Well, I'm not a boozer either, only I felt like a drink

tonight because I've just got back off my fifteen days. A
bloke deserves a drink after that.'

'I'll bet he does. What are you in?'

'Army. But I'll be done next year.'

'Shall you be glad?'

'Not much I wain't. I can't get out quick enough.'

'My sister married a man in the air force,' she told him.
'He looked ever so nice in his uniform. He's out now
though, and they've got a house up Wollaton. She's
expecting a baby next week.'

'Do you live up that way?' he asked, his drink not
touched.

'No,' she answered, 'up Broxtowe, on the estate. I like
living in them nice new houses. It's a long way from the
shops, but there's plenty of fresh air.' He suggested she
take the crisps to her family and come back to the bar. 'All
right' she said. He heard her say loudly to her mother that
she had met a friend from work and wanted to talk to him.
He drank.

She returns to him at the bar, and they chat further. Then:

'What do you do in the week?' he ventured. 'Do you ever
go to't pictures?'

She looked at him with brown suspicious eyes. 'Only on
Monday. Why?'

'That's funny, because I go out on a Monday night as
well to't pictures. I allus think Monday's the best night of
the week for that sort of thing, because I go for a drink and
see my pals at the week-end, and on the other days I have a
lot to do, mending my bike, or getting my tackle ready for
fishing. And Monday night is allus best for the pictures
because the new ones are on then. Which one do you go
to?'

'The Granby.'

'I go there sometimes on a Monday,' he said, 'and I've
never seen you before.'

'That's because hundreds of other people go as well,' she
answered facetiously.

'I'll see you tomorrow night at seven, then,' he said.

'Fast worker, aren't you? All right, but not on the back
row.'

'Why not? I can't see unless I sit right on the back row. If I get near the front the picture goes blurred. Something's wrong with my eyes, I suppose.'

'You want glasses,' she said, 'by the sound of it.'

And so it continues. We see the whole pick-up in front of us, and there's not a word or gesture out of place. The curious thing is that, although neither of them is being particularly 'clever' in the things they say or the subjects they talk about, the dialogue holds our attention all the way through, and we do get the sense that both Arthur and Doreen are politicians in the way they manipulate the conversation. A game is being played out in front of us. While it is through Arthur's eyes that we see the situation, and it is he who makes the cynical asides, and introduces the cinema idea, Doreen is evidently quite up to his manipulation.

In Britain at least, what you 'know' about someone has much to do with their social class, and that in turn has much to do with the way they speak. It is class ignorance that trips up Forster, and class knowledge which roots Sillitoe in the immediately believable. Forster has started off with a generalised idea about 'the working class', and tried to create characters to illustrate it. As a result, his scene is not 'rooted in the particular' — which is quite different from Sillitoe's pub conversation, in which he begins with two individuals who happen to be working class. But the scene does not set out to be 'An Illustration of Working Class Life', as Forster's feels it does. Sillitoe obeys, here at least, the two opening maxims of the chapter. He has started with a concrete situation, which is 'rooted in the particular.' And he has written from experience, from 'what he knows'.

What you know best: your own life

The most extreme form of writing about what you know is of course writing directly about your own life in the form of autobiography. Nobody knows your own life better than you do, certainly. But the common response to the idea of autobiography is 'oh, but my life's too boring for anybody else to want to read about it'. Well, two things could perhaps be said by way of a reply to that.

The first would be to make the essential point that it's the treatment you give your material, in this case your life story or a part of it, as much as the interest of your material itself that will make it appeal to the reader (and to you, the writer). The simple fact is that almost all writers inevitably draw directly upon their own lives for their materials. Hemingway's 'Nick Adams' stories and Dylan Thomas's memories of his Welsh boyhood are but two reminders of the fact that childhood, at least, is a domain we all share. Joyce's *A Portrait of the Artist as a Young Man* covers an outwardly uneventful youth, from infancy to the time he leaves university. It begins:

> Once upon a time and a very good time it was there was a moocow coming along the road and this moocow that was coming down along the road met a nicens little boy named baby tuckoo . . .
> His father told him that story: his father looked at him through a glass: he had a hairy face.

And it ends:

> April 26: Mother is putting my new secondhand clothes in order. She prays now, she says, that I may learn in my own life and away from home and friends what the heart is and what it feels. Amen. So be it. Welcome, O life! I go to encounter for the millionth time the reality of experience and to forge in the smithy of my soul the uncreated conscience of my race.

In the course of the book Joyce experiments with a marvellous variety of styles each of which captures the exact feeling of each period of his youth.

The second point about writing autobiography that needs to be made is one which is implied throughout this book: namely, that it no longer makes sense to think about the future of a piece of writing only in terms either of publication or of being left to rot in a drawer, as if there was nothing in between. So that if you feel only a limited number of people would be interested in your autobiographical writing, whether by virtue of their locality, or profession or whatever, that shouldn't discourage you in the least. Community bookshops and publishers in particular have been active in publishing both memoirs and creative writing. East London's Centerprise have published two volumes of *Working Lives*, a collection of writing about different trades and occupations by their practitioners in pre-war Hackney.

Word Power

Nobody can tell you how to write your autobiography. But an example might be of help to isolate one general point concerning technique:

Pre-1914 in the East End of London — drab to say the least. Two figures walking in the early morning streets. One, a woman dressed in the long dark skirt of the time and a nondescript hat. Around her shoulders a short, black cape, not even of the time, but of some years earlier, for some traces of embroidery still cling to the somewhat rusty coloured surface. Underneath the cape, half hidden by it, the woman carries an armful of newspapers. The other figure is a girl of fourteen, though rather small and childish looking for her age, and together they deliver the papers to various houses and shops until eventually they arrive, as they do every morning, at a door in a back alley-way which

is the stage door of the local music hall, the Hackney Empire. They are let in by a man who has evidently been there all night, as he is unshaven and has a muffler round his neck. Actually he is the night watchman and fireman. The three greet each other. They are my father, mother and I. Dad has just reached the stage of making an early morning jug of tea. It is hot and strong and we all partake of this exciting refreshment, which is a regular morning event.

This is how Emily Bishop begins 'Embroidery', her contribution to *Working Lives*. The use of the present tense, which gives the effect of an opening cinema shot, is a useful device to help create atmosphere and to give the reader a visual picture. While it is nothing elaborate, it is still a device, and, as such, artificial. It would be a mistake to assume that an autobiography must be free of 'artifice'. Just like anything written, it needs shaping, selecting, and cutting.

As a start, it might be wise to leave a full-scale autobiography for the moment, and try a few chapters about the parts of your life that strike you as the most potentially interesting to write about. Or use them as the basis for some short stories about childhood or growing up. You won't have to worry about sticking to the facts, change them in any way that seems useful, as long as they remain faithful to what *you* know about. Show them to friends or anybody you know who'd be interested —

16

and this applies to everything you write. It takes time to get over a natural sensitivity, even embarrassment, at having what you've written commented on. But the sooner the better.

The next chapter moves from you and what you know to a simple way of creating characters.

IDEAS FOR WRITING

Describe some of the things (you could confine yourself to your own house) which you regard with particular affection, or loathing. Try to avoid telling the reader directly how you feel about them, letting your emotions come through instead in the way you describe the objects.

In a few paragraphs, create a junk shop, or an abandoned loft. Describe the bits and pieces inside, either as a stranger to them, or the proprietor of the shop, or the former owner of the loft, so that some idea of you as a person emerges from the description.

Describe a person, real or fictitious, solely in terms of things. You don't have to be 'factual' about them, you could follow a pattern of 'When I think of X I think of . . .'

Minutely describe the sounds you hear going to sleep late at night, or in a fever. Try to capture the sense of drifting into sleep as you describe what you hear.

You wander into a house whose occupants you have never met. Trying to find out what kind of people they are, you go from room to room noting what you see. Describe this.

You enter a strange room in the dark. There are no lights. You have to get to know your way around, and what's in the room, by touch, aided by smell. Describe that process.

Try a description based mostly on images of a few hours at a fairground, or at the seaside, even of a city in the rush hour, or the trivial events you witness on the street below your window.

Make a brief list of some of the events which have been important to you in your life which would be interesting to write about. (Your 21st birthday party may have been important to you, but would not necessarily be right as the subject for a short story.) Childhood, certainly, is full of moments whose significance we only understand after the event. When you have made your list, which itself should prove a useful exercise, select a few and either write them up as chapters of an autobiography, or as short stories. (See 'What you know best: your own life'.)

As examples of writing specifically about childhood, you might read the following short stories:

Ernest Hemingway	Indian Camp
	The Killers
	A Day's Wait
Frank O'Connor	My Oedipus Complex
Saki	The Lumber Room
	Shredni Vashtar

2 Finding a voice

In the beginning stages of writing, it is advisable not only to keep a hold on the concrete world and limit yourself to what you know (chapter 1) but also to limit the area you wish to explore in your writing. Rather than thinking about how to present a group of people in a particular situation, and worrying about the style in which you want to write this, (that is, the kind of voice with which you will speak to the reader), you might usefully restrict yourself to one character, and use *their* voice — or, in other words, write a monologue.

In a monologue, one person speaks to the reader. That one person is all you need. Of course he or she should be an interesting person, for whatever reason — the way they speak, what they think, or because of something that they've done or want to do. In writing a monologue you won't have to worry about too much else. Not your 'style', because someone else is speaking for you, and as the feeling of natural speech is important in a monologue your mind will be concentrated on the way people speak, which is basic to all writing. You won't be able to indulge in 'literary' turns of phrase that so often make the writer purr and the reader wince — not unless your speaker also happens to be given to literary turns of phrase as well, perhaps something to be avoided for the moment. The question, too, of 'plot', what shall I make happen, will be half dealt with. As is frequently said of drama, 'character is plot'. That can mean many things, but at a simple level, a reader can be made to feel a piece is 'going somewhere' simply by having a character interestingly revealed to him. There are as many possible monologues as there are people in the world, and many possible ways of telling them. For the moment we can define a 'monologue' as a piece in which the narrator's personality provides the main source of interest — as opposed to a 'short story told in the first person', in which we might expect other things (the plot, the setting, the dialogue and so on) to provide this.

This is the opening of Bill Naughton's 'Spiv in Love':

She was a bit of a drip was old Myra, but absolutely gone on me. If she hadn't have been I don't suppose I'd have looked on the same side of the street she was on, let alone take her out. But I'm like that I am. I can't turn my back on a woman who looks up to me and thinks I am somebody, even if, what you might say, I can't bear the sight of her otherwise. I must admit a bit of the old flannel goes a long way with me, especially if a woman tells me I dress well. I do like anything like that. Another thing I've got to have is a woman around that I can be off-hand with, blow my top with if I feel like it, and generally say what I want to, clean or dirty. Most women won't stand for it, because they ain't got the savvy to see it don't matter, and that once you've said what you want and done what you want, all the best what was underneath is on top. But them dames that can see it can make a bloke feel at home. Not that I like to go regular with that sort of woman — because as a rule they're on the scruffy side, and a bloke can't show 'em off to his mates in the dance hall or in the pubs, which I like to do with a woman — but if they ain't good enough for a steady, I do like to have one on the side as a fill-in.

Although I say it myself as shouldn't, I was dead smart when I first picked up Myra.

And he goes on to tell us in great detail what he was wearing that night. Never mind Myra for the moment. From the start, we are in the Spiv's world, his turns of phrase and tone of voice taking us right into the East End with him. The story goes on, fairly conventionally, to tell us how the spiv kept Myra 'on the side for a fill-in' and finally got a taste of his own medicine. What really holds our interest, though, is the way we find out more and more about the spiv, about his (generally outrageous) attitudes to women, dress and sexual relationships. His character is the mainspring of the plot.

In a short story told in monologue, the character of the narrator is often of overriding interest. The story we read is a glimpse into the narrator's world, and letting the character speak for himself is a very effective way of giving us that glimpse. Such is Muriel Spark's 'You Should Have Seen the Mess':

I am now more than glad that I did not pass into the Grammar School five years ago, although it was a disappointment at the time. I was always good at English, but not so good at the other subjects!!

I am glad that I went to the Secondary Modern School, because it was only constructed the year before. Therefore, it was much more hygienic than the Grammar School. The Secondary Modern was light and airy, and the walls were painted with a bright, washable gloss. One day, I was sent over to the Grammar School, with a note for one of the teachers, and you should have seen the mess! The corridors were dusty, and I saw dust on the window ledges, which were chipped. I saw into one of the classrooms. It was very untidy in there.

I am also glad that I did not go to the Grammar School, because of what it does to one's habits. This may appear to be a strange remark, at first sight. It is a good thing to have an education behind you, and I do not believe in ignorance, but I have had certain experiences, with educated people, since going out into the world.

I am seventeen years of age, and left school two years ago last month. I had my A certificate for typing, so got my first job, as a junior, in a solicitor's office. Mum was pleased at this, and Dad said it was a first-class start, as it was an old-established firm. I must say that when I went for the interview, I was surprised at the windows, and the stairs up to the offices were also far from clean. There was a little waiting room, where some of the elements were missing from the gas fire, and the carpet on the floor was worn. However, Mr Heygate's office, into which I was shown for the interview, was better. The furniture was old, but it was polished, and there was a good carpet, I will say that. The glass of the bookcase was very clean.

The girl speaking is a humourless (but not inhuman) little prig, with cast-iron notions about respectability that find their most frequent expression in her comments about cleanliness. Her manner of speaking is self-consciously 'correct': she says the Secondary Modern had only been 'constructed' the year before, she begins the next sentence with 'Therefore' (rather than 'so'), she is prissy in the way she refers to 'certain experiences, with educated people'. She is so besotted with 'respectability' that, as we see later in the story, she is unable to accept the fun and freedom offered her by a particular 'educated person'. But the reader can see past her blinkers to the possibilities beyond, and that makes it a very funny, and painful, story to read. Increasingly we feel we are reading two stories, events as seen by the speaker, and events as seen by us. This is a great advantage of the monologue form, and it's great fun to do. The events in themselves don't have to be dramatic: it is the difference between the two ways of seeing them that entertains the reader.

No plot at all

Even in such a short space, a monologue offers many opportunities. You could easily dispense with the idea of plot completely, and just try to let the character *speak*, about something or someone of importance to them. Although a monologue is obviously written, (by you), trying to capture the feel of the speaking voice, its rhythms and digressions, can be a help in convincing the reader of the reality of your character. Now if your character is, say, a model railway enthusiast, that may or may not make for an interesting monologue. If he says the conventional things about model railways then the reader is likely to be bored. But if his talking about model railways can be used to suggest his entire psychology, the way he looks at and deals with the world, then it might be interesting. Or there may be an idea, an event, a possibility, something that the speaker in your monologue thinks about all the time, which differentiates him or her from other people. In the piece opposite, I have imagined a man thinking about death. Obviously this is something that everybody thinks about at some time or other, but here I've tried to show a particular individual getting himself tied up in the ironies and paradoxes of preparing for death. I didn't think it necessary to specify where he lives, what he does for a living, and so on.

'Images of that horror'

Ripeness, as when your fingers cleanly strip the skin off a tangerine, no white bits in the fingernails, and the skin falls away obediently, leaving the perfect fruit bare and ready.

The skin, pitted and rubbery, complies with the fingers, can be neatly discarded, that's how it must be.

Today, I trod on a frog. Purely by accident of course, as I was opening the garden gate. Naturally, I put down my briefcase and lifted the frog onto the grass, where it sat quite still, its mottled, leathery sides contracting and expanding, its eyes unblinking, its innards trickling from the split in its rear. The eyes never closed, but the flanks became still. It was a moving, not to say inspiring, sight. I watched it all. No hysteria, no death rattle, just the knowledge that life was slipping out with the brown slime accumulating on the grass, and acceptance. It must have been after a spider, when my heel ended that. But it didn't matter. Animals are like that.

It doesn't scare me, you see. Oh, it used to. But when you think about it, it isn't that which is frightening. My wife used to complain, uneasily I thought, that the Elizabethans were 'so bloody morbid' putting their memento moris everywhere, a skull on a screen, a figure with a scythe on a wooden chest.

I used to be scared, certainly. There was one occasion when we had friends to dinner, including one sweet old lady who was leaving the party early as was her custom. I helped her to the door and she cried 'Oh bless you' and took my wrist in her skinny hands. As she beamed at me, I saw her dry, dying skin draped over her skull, and only two blank sockets where her eyes were, and her teeth bared and mouldy and revolting. When I went back into the dining room, all I was aware of was a bunch of skeletons nodding at each other, their knives and forks clashing on the china, their teeth gnashing at beef. My wife played a very good Lady Macbeth that night, and was exemplary in her handling of the guests.

It was a difficult period and I have to admit she was most understanding. She bore with me while I buried myself in Keats, the Jacobeans, Edgar Allan Poe, anybody who would tell me what I wanted to hear. Shakespeare's Troilus, the fool, obsessed me for a time. I even spent a night in a morgue, and she was patient of all my Gothic habits. There were times when I had to sleep in the spare room, because I couldn't stand the thought of our sacks, as I called them, rubbing together. And she was a greater support than any man might ask his wife to be.

Then I remember driving down the street and seeing a piece of scaffolding narrowly miss an unsuspecting pedestrian. I leapt out of the car, I suppose to see if he was all right, and found myself becoming quite furious with him, shouting at him and shaking him. He was so nonchalant. 'What if it had hit him, would he have been ready?' I shouted. 'Look mate, a miss is as good as a mile, see?' he said, and walked off.

And of course they're all like that. Take Lear for instance. They all go on about the 'birds in a cage business', but the whole thing comes over in the three perfect lines.

Kent   Is this the promised end?
Edgar   Or image of that horror?
Albany   Fall and cease.

Which brings me back to ripeness. The peel falling away from the fruit. Every day I look in the newspapers, and every day I find, a woman waiting to go to the dentist slips off the platform in front of a tube train, her fashionable heel caught in a crack: a man on holiday with his wife eats shellfish and dies, or stumbles during a cliff walk, or drowns in a sudden undertow. (They say that your whole life flashes before you as you drown, an illusion conveniently fostered by scared people.) It's all so appallingly sudden, so unexpected. Few of them know as much as the frog this afternoon. They just don't think, you see. My wife wouldn't think either, she was, in the end, like everyone else, pretend it isn't there. She was all very sympathetic when I was a bit loony, but once I started thinking about actually preparing myself, which is the only thing to do, she moved out. Other men, I've noticed, take new and younger wives.

Not me. I'm like a mountaineer, skilfully defiant but prepared. I have often considered living in San Francisco, that doomed city. It would please me to know that those fine skyscrapers would one day, soon, be split by huge cracks, and tumble, Babylonian, into the sea. But I went there once, and was sickened by the ignorant gaiety of the place. I had hoped that living in that city would be like climbing a mountain.

So instead I live here, and wait. I am ready for that moment. I am ripe.

It isn't much rooted in time and place, but then I think I wanted that. His obsession with being 'prepared' is precisely what keeps him from entering into the here and now. If the character's 'literariness', his quotations, his reading of poetry, is irritating, well, that's an essential part of him too. He's 'refined' all right, and one of the consequences is that he can't shrug his shoulders and get on with living. Instead he reads, broods, and prepares.

This quality of the speaker not being 'all there', in the every-day world, is even stronger in this last piece. Here we have just a few moments of an individual's life, no introduction, no conclusions. It was written by a student of mine, and is untitled.

The earth is brown. I don't know what kind of brown — one with a lot of yellow ochre mixed in it. It looks stale and worn in the evening sun.

The earth is strewn with flowers. They fall from the tree above me. On the branches of the tree they hang in bunches but on the ground they are all single and separate. They are lemon yellow in colour, but even though the flowers are dead now, the colour is fresh. I like the combination. Red brown ochre and vibrant yellow.

The flowers move restlessly over the ground, like some sleepy old flying carpet from the Arabian nights. All of a sudden they seem to freeze — not actually freeze because the petals vibrate — ever so slightly.

I walk away from the tree; I keep walking and the earth flows beneath my feet. I don't know why people stare so much. The children stare with large eyes, sometimes they laugh — I like the children. The other people look and quickly move their gaze. They try to look into my mind. I hate that. I pity them.

I come to the sea . . . It looks hard, metallic. Like some kind of amalgam. Liquid mercury, sprayed over in parts by platinum that shines coldly.

On the beach there is a barefoot boy selling bubbles. They are very pretty. There are so many of them. I follow one — it floats in the air in starts. Now up, up then down. It is reluctant to come down, touch the sand. It moves parallel to the ground for some distance and then all of a sudden I can't see it anymore.

The boy comes to me. I give him a coin. He gives me a loop like thing in return. It is a metallic wire in a circle with a small handle. I forgot to ask him how to make the bubbles and I cannot spot him now among the people.

The sea seems not to move at all. It is so still.

Admittedly some people find this fairly baffling. We don't know where or how old or what sex the speaker is, why (s)he is there or where s(he) is coming from. But these things aren't the only ones which help us to understand a person. What we *do* have is a glimpse into a very private world. It is a world of only partial comprehension of what is going on around the character. We can feel that in the way (s)he describes so carefully 'The earth is brown. I don't know what kind of brown . . .' yet so flatly, the details of the physical environment, the earth, the trees, the sea, the boy. The sentences are short, and generally make simple statements. It is as if the character has only a fragile hold on reality. People try to look into the person's mind: 'I hate that. I pity them.' There's something quite beautiful about the character's mental world, the way (s)he *responds* to these physical details, but something eerie too. There's a feeling of a dream about it, as if the reasons why any of these things should be aren't quite clear; but it seems to be the way the speaker always experiences the world. That's one of the great advantages of the monologue form: five minutes' first-hand experience is enough to take us into the whole consciousness of an individual.

These four monologues show a kind of progression along a scale, with at one end something absolutely realistic, with a strong 'social' slant ('Spiv in Love') and at the other something closer to a dream, a strictly private, inaccessible world ('The earth is brown . . .').

'Spiv in love' A familiar social type perfectly reproduced. Very much 'in the world'	'You Should Have Seen the Mess' A less easily identifiable social type, with particular obsessions. Interacting with the world in general.	'Images of that horror' Though obviously an 'educated' man, social position unimportant. His ideas more important than his world.	'The earth is brown...' The private world, not interacting with other people. Impossible to specify the social type, sex, or age of the speaker.

These distinctions are fairly crude — a monologue about an easily recognisable social type could perfectly well suggest a very private world, for instance. But the importance of the social world decreases, roughly speaking, in each story. The more 'private' or 'extraordinary' a person is, the less likely it is that the outside world, as defined and accepted by ordinary people, will play a significant part in their monologue. Assuming that, for the moment, you are primarily interested in looking at one character, rather than telling a full-blown story with a plot and so on, there are of course an infinite number of points along this scale for you to choose from — and no reason why you shouldn't shoot off either end, or make up a different scale of your own. Moreover, as the plot of a story develops and becomes more complex so too does the role of the narrator. Does the narrator know, for example, the whole truth about the events s(he) describes? Might the narrator have a vested interest in seeing things a particular way? This is looked at in more detail in chapter 6, 'Who's telling the story?'

27

IDEAS FOR WRITING

Write all these in a monologue form.

Imagine a particular person in a particular place, nothing extraordinary, perhaps someone sitting in the bar of their local waiting for the evening to start, or a music-crazy kid coming out of a rock concert, or someone in the act of *doing* something, playing darts, cutting the grass, sitting down to write a letter. Tell the reader what is going through their head. Keep it realistic, down-to-earth, thinking about the way your kind of person talks.

Write the thoughts of someone you've often seen, never spoken to, but feel you know. Include the details you know about them, imagine some more of your own. Their thoughts are wandering as they sit on the train or look out of the window.

Something obsesses you — the way your husband, or father comes in from work, the mess your flatmates make, the music from next door, a particular ritual you always go through with somebody, a particular activity you do. At times this obsession dominates your consciousness. Write about one of those times. Let the reader feel the force of that obsession.

You are an extraordinary person or creature in an extraordinary situation. You live at the bottom of a well, or behind a cupboard, you have known all Time, you are a spirit, a saint, a strange character from history. Speak for a few pages, and convince the reader of your existence by doing so.

Use any of the following passages as beginnings for your own monologues. Adapt them in any way you wish.
a) He's in the room below at the moment. He's been there half an hour. I heard him go in there, and I can hear him moving around in there now.

b) As you might imagine, you meet some funny blokes in my line of business. Like the other day, this geezer in a bowler hat flags me down and says 'Buckingham Palace — fast!' 'Oh yeah,' I think, getting into gear and moving off.

Half a minute later he jumps up and shouts through the partition 'D'you know what I've got in here?'
'No,' I says, 'I don't. Let me guess'

c) Three minutes to go. That should just be long enough. Take a deep breath. Stop trembling. That's right.

d) The upstairs room in the house opposite, above the one where the geraniums are, often has its blind drawn. Even on a sunny day like this morning. From where I am, I can see the stairs that lead up to that room, and every now and then someone goes up there.

e) Every morning the soldier is there. He knows I'm looking at him, and doesn't like it. He looks about nineteen. He holds his gun as if someone was going to come up and take it away from him.

3 Time to talk

Even if you have been quite successful in using someone else's voice in a monologue, you will face a quite new situation when you come to writing a dialogue between two or more people. A character in a monologue follows his own path, decides his own rhythms and areas of interest. In dialogue, each speaker instinctively reacts to the language, personality, social position, sex, tone of voice of the other, and can be seen to be doing so in what he says. The challenge of dialogue is enormous, and crucial: no good extended piece of writing can live without at least some of it, many good pieces (some of Hemingway's short stories, for instance) rely almost solely upon it. However powerful or subtle your writing may be, if you skimp on dialogue you run the risk of losing the feel of independent reality that all good fiction needs. The reader will begin to feel stifled by your personal viewpoint and want a *first-hand* knowledge of the people concerned. Otherwise the characters will remain shadowy and unreal, like people we have heard talked about but never met. For it is in hearing people speak that we get to know them best, or at least form a distinct impression of them, and understand something of the relationship between them.

It's an important feature of the classic nineteenth century novels, by writers like George Eliot, Dickens, Henry James, Tolstoy, Balzac, that they burst at the seams with dialogue. It's no coincidence that they adapt so well to television 'classic serials'. It isn't only that much of the dialogue can be transposed from the page to the screen: it is that a direct result of that wealth of dialogue is vivid, fully imaginable characters. And that makes for good television, good soap opera, and good reading. Why is it that Dickens' characters are such familiar figures on television, cinema, advertising, comic books? Largely because they talk so much, and talk in a highly personal, idiosyncratic way. It's a lot easier to film a Jane Austen novel than a novel like Albert Camus' *The Outsider*. A modern classic such as this is less concerned with characters in the ordinary sense of the word than with the narrator himself as a 'figure' and the ideas that are generated by his conflict with the ordinary world. This is not a failing on Camus' part, of course. It's a different kind of writing. But if you are keen to create a strong sense of the real, various, everyday world, the world out there rather than the one within, then a good measure of dialogue is essential.

Many people believe dialogue to be easy to write. It is. You can cover pages quickly and write exactly in the way people speak. But it won't necessarily be interesting. You have to be selective, letting the reader work on their own to fill in the picture. It isn't merely 'information' that dialogue should be conveying. There are usually more economical ways of getting that across. What a reader needs from dialogue is a sense of two or more people interacting, whether pleading, bargaining, probing, letting out their frustrations, not getting through to each other, being cold, loving, angry, perhaps conscious that what they're saying isn't exactly what they want to say. More than anything else you write, your dialogue has to be alive, has to feel unplanned, spontaneous, not entirely predictable. This is true whoever is speaking, even if they are abnormally articulate. It's often pointed out, for example, that Jane Austen's characters are rather more articulate than people in real life. That's true, but they never merely deliver speeches to each other, they're alert to what is moving below the surface. And if one of them isn't, and through his own conceit or insensitivity *is* delivering speeches, that quality is always comically present in their contributions to the conversation.

Here's a passage dealing with a fairly familiar situation, the adolescent boy who's fallen in love, and a possessive mother.

'Is she *so* fascinating that you must follow her all that way?' Mrs Morel was bitterly sarcastic. She sat still, with averted face, stroking, with a rhythmic, jerked movement, the black sateen of her apron. It was a movement that hurt Paul to see.
'I do like her,' he said, 'but —'
'*Like* her!' said Mrs Morel, in the same biting tones. 'It seems to me you like nothing and nobody else. There's neither Annie, nor me, nor anyone now for you.'

'What nonsense, Mother — you know I don't love her — I — I tell you I *don't* love her — she doesn't even walk with my arm, because I don't want her to.'

'Then why do you fly to her so often!'

'I *do* like to talk to her — I never said I didn't. But I *don't* love her.'

'Is there nobody else to talk to?'

'Not about the things we talk of. There's lots of things that you're not interested in, that —'

'What things?' Mrs Morel was so intense that Paul began to pant.

'Why — painting — and books. *You* don't care about Herbert Spencer.'

'No,' was the sad reply. 'And *you* won't at my age.'

'Well, but I do now — and Miriam does —'

'And how do you know,' Mrs Morel flashed defiantly, 'that *I* shouldn't? Do you ever try me?'

'But you don't, Mother, you know you don't care whether a picture's decorative or not; you don't care what *manner* it is in.'

'How do you know I don't care? Do you ever try me? Do you ever talk to me about these things, to try?'

'But it's not that that matters to you, Mother, you know it's not.'

'What is it, then — what is it, then, that really matters to me?' she flashed. He knitted his brows with pain.

'You're old, Mother, and we're young.'

He only meant that the interests of *her* age were not the interests of his. But he realized the moment he had spoken that he had said the wrong thing.

> from *Sons and Lovers* by D.H. Lawrence

How is it that dialogue like this manages to be so powerful, even out of context, when dealing with such a common conflict? I once asked a group of students to look at this passage, and they read it with great insight and sensitivity to what was going on, and awareness of the way the writer showed unspoken as well as spoken fears. One student later continued the dialogue herself:

'Yes, I am old. But I tell you I was young once, and I didn't go doing just as I liked. I had some respect for my mother.'
'Well . . . times have changed, mother.'
'A mother's love doesn't change.'
'But I can't stay around here with you all the time. I've got to be with my *own* friends. And I need her to talk to as well. Annie's all right, but Annie's my sister, and I . . .'
'And what's wrong with your sister? She learns art at school, if that's so important to you. Talk to her about Herbert Spencer, or whoever he is.'
'Sisters aren't the same. And besides, everybody else . . .'
'I don't care about everybody else. I'm your mother, and I don't think any girl can be so marvellous as to take you away from your family day in and day out. And there are plenty of books *here* for you to read.'
'No, mother. It isn't the same.'
'Or the public library.'
Paul shook his head. Mrs Morel raised her voice in anger.
'Why is it that kids today want it all their own way? We were *happy* to spend time with our family . . . Oh, I don't care. Go to her, if she's so marvellous. Only don't come running to me every five minutes for your bed and board. Let her provide that for you — then we'll see if she's so marvellous.'

And so on. To continue another writer's dialogue, particularly when it comes from the middle of a full-scale novel, is probably not a very worthwhile exercise: arguably the mother and son here become different people when 'scripted' by a different person. But the results are interesting to compare with the original. Does the student's continuation maintain the standard of Lawrence's dialogue? Well, no, sadly. The extraordinary thing about Lawrence's is that although Mrs Morel says some pretty harsh things, which Paul does too in a clumsy way, we pick up quickly that her heart is breaking beneath her aggressive manner. Yet while Paul denies his love for the girl one minute, and uncertainly tries to defend his relationship with her the next, Mrs Morel doesn't let up. She seizes on anything she can, desperately, first with her aggressive 'What things?', then comes back again immediately when Paul seems to have a simple, conclusive answer with 'And how do you know . . . that *I* shouldn't? Do you ever try me?' And this is just after she has given her pathetic but also, we might say, manipulative answer 'No . . . and *you* won't at my age.' It is in the illogicality of her aggressiveness that we see how frightened she is.

In Lawrence's dialogue the struggle is intense, poignant, above all confused, with a marvellous balance of the classic roles that mother and son play, with the feel of two complex individuals working out where they stand with each other. In the continuation, we have only the former: the dialogue has degenerated into one about the generation gap, a row between any selfish son and any grouchy old mother. No doubt the generation gap was something very close to the student's heart. And surely to Lawrence's too. But so also, to Lawrence, was the mystery of these two particular individuals, and the power of sex, and Mrs Morel's failed marriage, and Paul's uncertainties about the girl, and . . . . This is not to sneer at the student. She herself was completely aware that her dialogue lacked any spark: and realised by the time she finished writing that her idea of continuing the dialogue wasn't a very fruitful one. She had been struck by the way the mother and son picked up what the other had just said, challenging, repeating, rejecting, and there are traces of this quality in her own dialogue. Certainly this is better than planning two people's speeches, chopping them up into blocks of a few sentences and distributing them to their respective speakers. Good dialogue must have the illusion of being organic, self-generating.

Keep yourself out

It is normally part of Lawrence's style to be bold in his commentary upon the dialogue, to direct the reader's attention and sympathy. Here in fact he interrupts the dialogue very infrequently, neither with comment nor 'stage directions'. The mention of the mother jerkily stroking her apron, for instance, is a sufficient visual clue to the tension in the air. He takes us inside Paul's mind at the crucial moment to tell us what Paul *means* when he tells his mother that she is old and they are young, but otherwise the argument takes place before us as if it were on stage. This helps to give the dialogue and the characters that feeling of independent life mentioned at the beginning of the chapter, a feeling which is one of the attractions of a well-written play, in which it *seems* there is no writer intervening between us and the characters he has created. (This isn't only because of the 'visual aid' effect of flesh and blood people on the stage: watching a bad play can give you an uncomfortable feeling of a struggle going on between the living actor and the lifeless, stereotyped part he has to play.) It's a result of presenting character entirely through dialogue and action. Writing which won't let the dialogue stand on its own is at best irritating, at worst gives the sense of the writer being more interested in him/herself than what's going on in the story:

'But Steve, who'll cook your Christmas dinner?' Maud protested. I forced a weak smile and reminded her that I cooked for the three of us every weekend. But my sister-in-law brushed by words aside with an imperious sweep of her arm. 'Christmas is different' she pronounced dogmatically. 'If you refuse to bring the children here, Rose will come round and look after you, won't you, Rose?'

Her daughter looked up from her library book. 'If that's what Steve wants,' she replied flatly. 'Of course he does,' Maud said. 'A woman's touch is essential at this time of year.'

My eyes narrowed. 'Why don't you come too?' I ventured craftily.

She folded her arms across her bosom. 'Certainly not,' she boomed. 'My place is in my own home'

I glanced across at Rose but she quickly averted her eyes, embarrassed. She knew as well as I the game her mother was playing.

In this kind of writing (the passage is from a magazine story) nothing is ever said 'straight': Maud 'protests', then 'brushes his words aside with an imperious sweep of her arm', then 'pronounces dogmatically', then 'booms', having first folded her arms across her bosom. The narrator 'forces a weak smile' then 'ventures craftily', with eyes narrowed. The daughter 'replies flatly.' But what has the reader gained by having so many subtleties of expression drawn to his attention? Nothing at all. While there is nothing wrong with what they are *saying* to each other the fact that this conversation is introducing the central idea of the story (the matchmaking game of the booming,

35

imperious, protesting Maud) seems to have led the author to
write this way in an attempt to make the writing more *vivid*. The
result though is not a vivid sense of reality but a vivid sense of
the writer's notions of his own vocabulary. Try reading five
pages of this at a stretch. You can't make dialogue interesting by
finding a hundred different words for 'said'.

Compare this with the following passage from Ernest Hemingway's short story 'Hills like White Elephants'. We are told
that somewhere in dusty central Spain, a couple are sitting
waiting for a train to come in to an almost deserted station.

The woman brought two glasses of beer and two felt pads.
She put the felt pads and the beer glasses on the table and
looked at the man and the girl. The girl was looking off at
the line of hills. They were white in the sun and the country
was brown and dry.

'They look like white elephants,' she said.
'I've never seen one.' The man drank his beer.
'No, you wouldn't have.'
'I might have,' the man said. 'Just because you say I
wouldn't have doesn't prove anything.'
The girl looked at the bead curtain. 'They've painted
something on it,' she said. 'What does it say?'
'Anis del Toro. It's a drink.'
'Could we try it?'
The man called 'listen' through the curtain. The woman
came out from the bar.
'Four reales.'
'We want two Anis del Toros.'
'With water?'
'Do you want it with water?'
'I don't know,' the girl said. 'Is it good with water?'
'It's all right.'
'You want them with water?' asked the woman.
'Yes, with water.'
'It tastes like liquorice,' the girl said and put the glass down.
'That's the way with everything.'
'Yes,' said the girl. 'Everything tastes of liquorice.
Especially all the things you've waited so long for, like
absinthe.'
'Oh, cut it out.'

'You started it,' the girl said. 'I was being amused. I was having a fine time.'
'Well, let's try and have a fine time.'
'All right. I was trying. I said the mountains looked like white elephants. Wasn't that bright?'
'I wanted to try this new drink. That's all we do, isn't it — look at things and try new drinks?'
'I guess so.'
The girl looked across at the hills.

Apart from the extreme unobtrusiveness of the writer — there's hardly a word which is not spoken directly by the man or the girl — what is striking here is how the conversation remains interesting to the reader despite the fact that they hardly seem to be talking 'about' anything. The tension in the situation appears in the importance the girl attaches to her little comparison, the indifference of the man towards it, their uneasy knowledge of both these things, the rhythms and repetitions and weariness of 'looking at things and trying new drinks.' So that we know that this is a couple who have known each other too long. And all this without a word of reference to the past, simply from the 'feel' of the dialogue.

Words and actions

Apart from the girl looking at the line of hills, there is not a gesture described in the passage above. That's the way Hemingway liked to write, and said so. Obviously, however, what people are doing can be as important as what they're saying. While we don't need to be told every time a woman folds her arms across her bosom, sometimes that gesture may in fact deepen our understanding of what she is saying. I don't think in the magazine story above it does. It simply isn't necessary. Maud's firmness is quite evident enough. But it might if such a gesture of firmness were unusual in the character, or done defensively, or out of social embarrassment. To risk a generalisation, physical gestures or tones of voice don't really need describing if they could be inferred from the dialogue. What follows is an example of words and actions being delicately used together to contribute to a single effect. The central character, Stephen, is visiting his ex-wife to arrange for their daughter to visit him. He expects his daughter to answer the door, but is met by his wife:

She had the advantage of three concrete steps and she glared down at him, waiting for him to speak. He had nothing ready for her.

'Is . . . is Miranda there?' he said finally. 'I'm a little late,' he added, and taking his chance, advanced up the steps. At the very last moment she stepped aside and opened the door wider.

'She's upstairs,' she said tonelessly as Stephen tried to squeeze by without touching her. 'We'll go in the big room.' Stephen followed her into the comfortable, unchanging room, lined from floor to ceiling with books he had left behind. In one corner, under its canvas cover, was his grand piano. Stephen ran his hand along its curving edge. Indicating the books he said, 'I must take all these off your hands.'

'In your own good time,' she said as she poured sherry for him. 'There's no hurry.' Stephen sat down at the piano and lifted the cover.

'Do either of you play it now?' She crossed the room with his glass and stood behind him.

'I never have the time. And Miranda isn't interested now.' He spread his hands over a soft, spacious chord, sustained it with the pedal and listened to it die away.

'Still in tune, then?'

'Yes.' He played more chords, he began to improvise a melody, almost a melody. He could happily forget what he **had come** for and be left alone to play for an hour or so, his piano.

'I haven't played for over a year,' he said by way of explanation. His wife was over by the door now about to call out to Miranda, and she had to snatch back her breath to say, 'Really? It sounds fine to me.' 'Miranda,' she called 'Miranda, Miranda,' rising and falling in three notes, the third note higher than the first, and trailing away inquisitively. Stephen played the three note tune back, and his wife broke off abruptly. She looked sharply in his direction.

'Very clever.'

'You know you have a musical voice,' said Stephen without irony. She advanced farther into the room.

'Are you still intending to ask Miranda to stay with you?' Stephen closed the piano and resigned himself to hostilities.

'Have you been working on her then?' She folded her arms.

'She won't go with you. Not alone anyway.'

'There isn't room in the flat for you as well.'

'And thank God there isn't.' Stephen stood up and raised his hand like an Indian chief.

'Let's not,' he said. 'Let's not.' She nodded and returned to the door and called out to their daughter in a steady tone, immune to imitation.

from 'In Between the Sheets' by Ian McEwan

Here, words and actions combine to give a sharp sense of a couple familiar with each other but also extremely tense. Stephen is able to predict, and forestall, a row at the end, though it is his own fondness for the ironic gesture that has nearly caused it. There is a hint of the flirtatious *and* the nostalgic about his picking out the notes of his wife's call on the piano, and his comment on her voice. She pours him sherry but stands behind him at the piano. She is polite to him one moment, breaking off to compliment him on his playing, aggressive to him the next when he tells her there is no room for her in his flat. His going to the piano is both something to do in an awkward moment but also gives him a fleeting promise of relaxation and happiness. Most importantly, they don't sit and talk to each other, both finding things to do while they speak, in the way that anxious people do, but also in the way that a husband and wife might do in their own home. And in this passage, the folding of arms *is* important. It's the wife defensively drawing up battle lines against her husband. She is *expecting* trouble, which is one of the things that makes the situation so tense.

As always, there are no iron rules to be made. As always, you should become aware of how the writers you like go about it — for example in the proportion of dialogue to narrative, in the way they introduce a passage of dialogue, in the extent to which they comment upon what their characters are saying, whether they present conversations in their entirety or merely a few exchanges to give the feel of a situation at a particular time. Two things can perhaps be adopted as provisional resolutions. Firstly, don't aim for total realism at the risk of boring your reader with everyday chat. While it's got to be the kind of thing people might actually say to each other, it doesn't have to be the kind of thing that people say to each other every five minutes. Select, and edit. Secondly, aim in general to keep yourself out of the conversation and give the characters a chance to stand on their own. Readers can infer from straight dialogue much more than might be supposed — and anyway, a reader should have some work to do, whether in guessing people's motives or feelings, or background, or subconsciously predicting the course of events. It's one of the things that makes a reader engage with the material, and makes reading rewarding.

Can you hear me?

One of the features of the passages quoted above is that they all show people in conflict, and in the Lawrence and the Hemingway at least, unable to 'communicate' with each other. Of course, conflict has always been the essence of a good story and it's an important aspect of modern writing, particularly drama, that people's inability to communicate is as important as their ability to do so. We need to consider for a moment what we mean by communicating. Let us say that two (or more) people communicate when they know what they want to say, and say it, and understand what the other person is saying. They can be in the most violent disagreement with each other and still be communicating. We might then say that Lawrence's Paul Morel and his mother are *not* fully communicating. Their relationship at this stage is far too confused. When Paul says 'You're old mother, and we're young', what he meant is that 'the interests of her age were not the interests of his'. But the effect of his words is disastrous. In the student's continuation, however, it is more a case of two people simply disagreeing about how a son should behave towards his mother. As I mentioned earlier, Jane Austen's characters, drawn from a social class where a high premium was placed on being articulate, generally don't have much trouble expressing themselves. The Russian playwright

Chekhov at the turn of the century was among the first to show that what is not said is as valuable as what is. His characters spend a lot of their time on stage not getting through to each other, and much of the audience's interest lies in seeing exactly in what ways and for what reasons they aren't. Reading modern literature very much involves responding to what is going on below the level of actual speech. Why is it so important to the girl, for example, that the man isn't interested in hills looking like white elephants?

Eventually, however, the writer may come to consider the question 'How do I portray through dialogue two people who actually do communicate quite well and *are* getting through to each other? Perhaps they even love each other!' 'Good' things are notoriously difficult to depict in writing. Good relationships so easily appear sentimental, good people easily appear cardboard saints, like the moral-religious heroines of George Eliot, or superhumanly tolerant, understanding, sympathetic drips. It might be interesting to go back to *Sons and Lovers*, since we have already seen the two central characters clashing. Here we see them in a sort of natural harmony. Mrs Morel has just been out shopping. Paul is at home painting.

'Oh!' she sighed, smiling at him from the doorway.

'My word, you *are* loaded!' he exclaimed, putting down his brush.

'I am!' she gasped. 'That brazen Annie said she'd meet me. *Such* a weight!'

She dropped her string bag and her packages on the table.

'Is the bread done?' she asked, going to the oven.

'The last one is soaking,' he replied. 'You needn't look, I've not forgotten it.'

'Oh, that pot man!' she said, closing the oven door. 'You know what a wretch I've said he was? Well, I don't think he's quite so bad.'

'Don't you?'

The boy was attentive to her. She took off her little black bonnet.

'No. I think he can't make any money — well, it's everybody's cry alike nowadays — and it makes him disagreeable.'

'It would *me*,' said Paul.

'Well, one can't wonder at it. And he let me have — how much do you think he let me have *this* for?'

She took the dish out of its rag of newspaper, and stood looking on it with joy.

'Show me!' said Paul.

The two stood together gloating over the dish.

'I *love* cornflowers on things,' said Paul.

'Yes, and I thought of the teapot you bought me . . .'

'One and three,' said Paul.

'Fivepence!'

'It's not enough, mother.'

'No. Do you know, I fairly sneaked off with it. But I'd been extravagant, I couldn't afford any more. And he needn't have let me have it if he hadn't wanted to.'

'No, he needn't need he,' said Paul, and the two comforted each other from the fear of having robbed the pot man.

'We c'n have stewed fruit in it,' said Paul.

'Or custard, or a jelly,' said his mother.

'Or radishes and lettuce,' said he.

'Don't forget that bread,' she said, her voice bright with glee.

Paul looked in the oven; tapped the loaf on the base.

'It's done,' he said, giving it to her.

She tapped it also.

'Yes,' she replied, going to unpack her bag. 'Oh, and I'm a wicked extravagant woman. I know I s'll come to want.'

He hopped to her side eagerly, to see her latest extravagance. She unfolded another lump of newspaper and disclosed some roots of pansies and of crimson daisies.

'Four penn'orth!' she moaned.

'How *cheap*!' he cried.

'Yes, but I couldn't afford it *this* week of all weeks.'

'But lovely!' he cried.

'Aren't they!' she exclaimed, giving way to pure joy. 'Paul, look at this yellow one, isn't it — and a face just like an old man!'

'Just!' cried Paul, stooping to sniff. 'And smells that nice! But he's a bit splashed.'

He ran in the scullery, came back with the flannel, and carefully washed the pansy.

'*Now* look at him now he's wet!' he said.

'Yes!' she exclaimed, brimful of satisfaction.

Mrs Morel is half guilty, half triumphant about what she has bought. But her guilt disappears at Paul's excited approval. They share their delight in the pot, the flowers, the baked bread — and each other. They are high on each other's company. They are not talking *about* their relationship, they are living it. And within the context of the novel they are supporting each other: Mrs Morel's husband would have shown only anger at her extravagance. Most people (particularly British people) don't like talking about how much they like somebody or how much they value their relationship with them. They show it, if at all, in the things they do together, and in their tone of voice. Lawrence captures both these perfectly. The action is wholly spontaneous — Paul is not at all bothered about being interrupted in his painting — and the speech is excited, sentences not even waiting to be finished:

'Paul look at this yellow one, isn't it — and a face just like an old man!'

Paul *runs* into the scullery, and there is real affection, for the flower but also for his mother, in his '*Now* look at him now he's wet!'

IDEAS FOR WRITING

Write as many of these in straight, uninterrupted dialogue as you can. Each idea describes a situation in which two or more people talk to each other.

Two burglars are making a midnight haul in a country mansion. They begin to disagree about what they should take.

A woman alone in a house answers the telephone to a young man who fancies her daughter and of whom she does not approve. He tries to talk her round.

43

A small child asks some difficult questions of a grandparent.

A man returns home late. His wife delicately questions him, trying to pick up clues about where he has been and what, if anything, is 'going on'.

A computer dating agency has arranged a meeting between two people. There has been some mistake in the files.

Two ex-lovers bump into each other after some years at a party. Both their new escorts are present and potentially within earshot.

Members of a family discuss a lodger who has been living with them for a few weeks.

Use any of the following passages as beginnings for your own dialogues, or adapt them in any way you wish.
a) 'I want to . . .'
   'Yes I know you do.'
   'But you won't let me.'
   'It's hardly a question of you needing my permission.'
b) 'I suggest you forget about the whole thing.'
   The girl looked at her mother.
   'Do you?'
c) Brady and the girl looked at each other. There was a long silence.
   'Is this it?' she said.

A workman arrives at the door to do some work in a house, work which involves looking around the different rooms to begin with. Write not only the spoken dialogue between the workman and whoever shows him around, but also their thoughts during the conversation.

A mother and son are being interviewed by a local authority official. The mother and son have one way of speaking to the official and another of speaking to each other (in forms of dialect, slang or simply tone of voice).

A one-way conversation: a zoo keeper talks to the animals as he goes the rounds.

4 Writing about people

Don't tell, show

There is a sense in which it is meaningless to separate writing about people from any other kind of writing. Just as there is no special way to write about cats, or revolutions, or snow, there is no special way to write about people. Some text books frequently exhort you to USE VIVID WORDS as if this were the key to making people 'come alive'. The question to ask is 'come alive for what, and how?' It depends on what you want to 'do' with a character, and that depends on the kind of story you want to write, and the character's role within it. You will not want to describe in detail every waiter who serves your hero a cup of coffee — but if your hero is feeling threatened by the world then to describe the waiter's contemptuous manner may help to create the desired atmosphere of oppression. The description of the waiter is not done for its own sake, but because it makes him play a part in the story.

This is the beginning of a murder story:

> 'Did you have a good day at work, darling,' said Jeff, in his deep rich voice. Jeff Bridges was tall and well-built. His eyes, a sparkling chocolate brown and his hair, a deep brown with a hint of blond. His wife Jenny, also tall and slender, spoke in her soft and gentle voice. 'Sure. It was swell.' She had soft, curly blond hair and deep sea blue eyes. Jeff and Jenny were attracted to each other as soon as they met. 'How about you, honey?' she asked. 'It was okay,' Jeff replied.

The writer is making a gallant effort to make her characters 'come alive' for the reader, but the question 'come alive for what' has not been thought about. It is quite unnecessary to know what Jeff and Jenny look like, since their only function is to oil the wheels of a complicated whodunnit plot. (They also seem to inhabit a world based on advertising rather than on reality). Here is another opening:

> Krebs went to the war from a Methodist college in Kansas. There is a picture which shows him among his fraternity brothers, all of them wearing exactly the same height and style collar. He enlisted in the Marines in 1917 and did not return to the United States until the second division returned from the Rhine in the summer of 1919.
>
> There is a picture which shows him on the Rhine with two German girls and another corporal. Krebs and the corporal look too big for their uniforms. The German girls are not beautiful. The Rhine does not show in the picture.
>
> By the time Krebs returned to his home town in Oklahoma the greeting of heroes was over. He came back much too late. The men from the town who had been drafted had all been welcomed elaborately on their return. There had been a great deal of hysteria. Now the reaction had set in. People seemed to think it was rather ridiculous for Krebs to be getting back so late, years after the war was over.

There are no 'vivid words' here. Nor is there any description of what Krebs looks like. What Hemingway has done instead is to give us two photographs, both of which show Krebs as an ordinary guy — college fraternity member in one, off-duty soldier in the other. In the second picture, there is a note of awkwardness: 'Krebs and the corporal look too big for their uniforms. The German girls are not beautiful.' This is taken further in the next paragraph. Krebs' return is mistimed. He is an ordinary guy, but he is also a misfit, and that feeling, of being in the wrong place at the wrong time, is what Krebs, and the story 'Soldier's Home', is about. The device of describing two such photographs, before we properly meet Krebs, beautifully and economically places him in a context, and directs our expectations so that we 'read' him in the right way when we do meet him.

One way of making the reader imagine a character in the way you want is to show the character in action, rather than writing a genuine description of them. Even Krebs is doing something in a specific time and place in the photographs described (for instance, posing for a fraternity photograph) which tells the reader about him. This is Dickens in *Great Expectations*:

> My sister had a trenchant way of cutting our bread-and-butter for us, that never varied. First, with her left hand she jammed the loaf hard and fast against her bib — where it sometimes got a pin into it, and sometimes a needle, which we afterwards got into our mouths. Then she took some butter (not too much) on a knife and spread it on the loaf, in an apothecary kind of way, as if she were making a plaister — using both sides of the knife with a slapping dexterity, and trimming and moulding the butter off round the crust. Then, she gave the knife a final smart wipe on the edge of the plaister, and then sawed a very thick round off the loaf; which she finally, before separating from the loaf, hewed into two halves, of which Joe got one, and I the other.

We are *shown her* in a visual way, rather than *told about her*. Her way of cutting the bread for her family is far more telling for the reader than a biographical sketch about her. This is not an essay, but drama enacted before us.

This cannot be separated from the points made in the previous chapter about dialogue. There it was suggested that good dialogue gives the reader first-hand experience of the characters in a book. Dialogue after all is only another way of 'writing about people'. And whether a character is doing something or talking to somebody, the reader is being shown rather than told. There will be very many different ways in which you as the writer can comment on your characters, directly or indirectly, or abstain from comment altogether. But comment alone will not make your characters convincing.

Someone you know

It could be that you are interested in writing accounts of people you actually know. This may seem easier, but it poses its own difficulties. When writing fiction, an author (as was particularly evident in the Hemingway story) generally has some idea what he wants to do with a character, and therefore will concentrate on bringing out certain qualities which will be of importance in the work as a whole. This is not so easy when writing a sketch of someone you know. Will you end up with a rather vague, generalised description because you haven't an 'angle', a 'slant', to help you select the relevant details? That 'angle', of course, may emerge once you start writing, and you see which things work on paper. Here is a writer describing someone they see frequently; a character at the local market, Willy the watch-mender.

Willy's full height is very nearly five foot. He is quite bald on top and what hair is left round the sides is rather sparse, and white. He has a round pink face and over each eye rests a silver eyebrow that is long overdue for a trim. His ravaged nicotine stained moustache seems to droop in defeat onto a protruding red bottom lip. As he sits at his stall, his grey shabby jacket clings tightly to his shoulders, and sharply flares out as it reaches his rather global middle. All the time Willy works, he talks, laughs, and tells jokes to the waiting customers around him. This sort of behaviour of Willy's may give a newcomer to the market the impression that Willy's work is very slip-shod. But on the contrary Willy gives a first class service on the spot and charges only a fraction of what the large high street jewellers charge. Not only that, all the entertainment is free. He will give a running commentary at times of just what is wrong with the watch and what he intends doing about it, and what he is doing at the moment.

'Yes,' he will start, as he removes the back of the watch. 'Yes, the pallet's a bit sticky. Hello, your balance is a bit loose an' all.'

Willy's head would be well down now, his eyeglass buried into the socket of his eye, as his face wrinkles around it. His shoulders well up almost touching his ears, as he probes deep into the recesses of the timepiece. His head and shoulders still firmly in the working position. 'Not been cleaned for months 'as it?' Willy would enquire reprimandingly. While the owner shamefully shakes his head.

If you are alert enough you will notice that Willy's head will at frequent intervals make sudden two second dives under the stall. He will usually make this dive just after a joke has been told and everyone is overcome with hilarious laughter, or he may wait until some other distraction takes place. Willy usually comes up smacking his lips or burping.

But be warned. It is no good going to Willy with a repair if you are in a hurry. For it seems that Willy gives talking and diving priority over watch repairing.

Most customers have been going to Willy for years, and they are like old friends. He will hand a repaired watch back to its owner. 'Firty bob George'.

'Firty bob,' George would reply in mock surprise, as he addresses the audience, and holds the watch up to view. 'Look at that, he only cleaned the bleeding fing. Feiving old git, it's daylight robbery that's what it is. Not coming here no bleeding more.' ... This fresh bit of excitement gives Willy another opportunity for one of his quick and crafty dives, for the audience are now turned towards the departing customer. On becoming upright Willy burps and selects a watch from one of the dozen that are held out towards him. He gives the timepiece the usual shake and puts it to one of his red ears. His brow wrinkles and his eyes disappear under the silvery brows. In seconds the watch is in a thousand pieces on Willy's table. And the poor nervestruck owner looks on as Willy holds the smallest of screws in his tweezers, and rocks with convulsive laughter at a joke he has just told the audience. Everyone in the crowd is thoroughly enjoying all this, except of course the poor apprehensive looking fellow who owns the watch. Gradually Willy calms down, the audience too, and the poor nervous chap becomes a little more relaxed. Willy's head goes down, his shoulders move upwards, his face wrinkles round his eyeglass. Suddenly he hesitates, straightens up, takes out the eyeglass and looks questioningly at the tweezers.

He looks back at the audience, then back at the tweezers. He looks back at the audience, and back at the tweezers again.

'It's gorn,' he announces. 'It's gorn.'

The poor panic stricken owner was seen to go completely livid as his trembling white hands clasped each other, and the audience joined in a mass search of Willy's stall. Here was yet another opportunity for a quick dive. And Willy didn't miss it.

Ron Barnes, from *Hackney Writers' Workshop Vol. 1*

Willy is presented to us in action, a chaotic, quick-witted king of his market patch. There are plenty of marvellous details (his reprimanding manner with his terrified customers, the shoulders up to the ears with concentration), but two things in particular stick out. One is the short but telling physical description, including the 'silver eyebrow long overdue for a trim' which gives Willy a touch of the wild and devilish. The other is what I think is the best detail of all, because so extraordinary and individual — the dives under the table for a quick nip. It's the kind of thing that has sharp visual impact on the reader, and Ron Barnes seems to have known this, as it forms the central 'theme' the 'angle', almost, in the sketch: whenever there is an event which distracts attention, down he goes. It's often the quick brush stroke of a character in action rather than the painstaking detail that makes a character real. The portrait is a vivid one also because *we* have to guess what Willy is actually doing in his 'dives' — nowhere are we actually told. The writer is only reporting what he sees — he is showing, not telling, and the result, an element of detective work for the reader, is very satisfying.

Characters in action

Returning to fiction, here is a famous literary walk:

Two young men came down the hill of Rutland Square. One of them was just bringing a long monologue to a close. The other, who walked on the verge of the path and was at times obliged to step in to the road, owing to his companion's rudeness, wore an amused, listening face. He was squat and ruddy. A yachting cap was shoved far back from his forehead, and the narrative to which he listened made constant waves of expression break forth over his face from the corners of his nose and eyes and mouth. Little jets of wheezing laughter followed one another out of his convulsed body. His eyes, twinkling with cunning enjoyment, glanced at every moment towards his companion's face. Once or twice he rearranged the light waterproof which he had slung over one shoulder in toreador fashion. His breeches, his white rubber shoes, and his jauntily slung waterproof expressed youth. But his figure fell into rotundity at the waist, his hair was scant and grey, and his face, when the waves of expression had passed over it, had a ravaged look.

'Well! . . . That takes the biscuit!'

His voice seemed winnowed of vigour; and to enforce his words he added with humour:

'That takes the solitary, unique, and, if I may so call it, recherché biscuit!'

He became serious and silent when he had said this.

The two characters are introduced in the middle of an everyday action: the story concerns the mean, loveless friendship between the two men-about-town. One is holding forth with confidence, even rudeness, the other nervously approves and flatters. So the two men are shown in active relationship to each other, they are placed in a context which defines them: that one talks and the other listens. As he listens he has to bob deferentially on and off the pavement. He has an appearance of joviality and youth, but his face reveals him to be 'ravaged'. He isn't entirely sure when his friend has finished telling his story. His comment is a straightforward piece of boot-licking, and as if he knew it he digs around for something more positive, more 'clever' to say — and adds the clumsy and affected 'That takes the solitary, unique and if I may so call it, recherché biscuit.' This only makes him look a bigger fool than he already feels. 'He became serious and silent when he said this.' His nervousness, his insecurity, run right through this short description.

While 'introduce characters in action' may be a fairly useful guideline, it certainly isn't an infallible one — which of course is true of any 'rule' about writing. In the same stunning collection of short stories, *Dubliners*, Joyce does something quite different. He uses another quite common device, that of introducing the central character by first describing the room in which he lives, whose objects, arranged with immaculate tidiness, tell us a great deal about the man. At other times a writer may deliberately want to keep a character shadowy, rather than vivid. The enigmatic figure of Kurtz in Joseph Conrad's 'Heart of Darkness' is an example. He is a character about whom the narrator hears extraordinary tales, and about whom he thinks obsessively, so that when the narrator and the reader finally meet Kurtz he has become as much an idea or symbol as an actual person.

Detectives, dreamers, outlaws

The previous sentence brings us back to the opening point of the chapter, that what matters is not merely to make a character 'come alive', but to think about the question 'come alive for what, and how?' In the examples we have looked at so far, the writer has wanted to make the reader believe in the tangible existence of his characters. In this sense, he has adopted a *realistic* approach to writing. Kurtz, however, is perhaps more important as an 'idea', of an educated European being taken over by the primitive forces of the remote heart of Africa, than he is as an individual person. It is the shadowy area between people-as-real-individuals, and people-as-ideas, that is the subject of this final section.

The notion of a person being other than a 'real individual' may seem a strange one. But there is a sense in which many people have a power over our imaginations, and therefore a kind of *imaginative* reality: Napoleon, for example, or Billy the Kid, or Marilyn Monroe, (not to mention our own husbands, or girlfriends) exist in our imaginations as strongly as they did in history. And there is much creative enjoyment to be got from exploring this 'imaginative reality'.

In 1935 the South American writer Jorge Luis Borges published his first book, called *A Universal History of Infamy*. Despite its imposing title the book was in fact a little collection of biographical sketches of obscure or infamous villains of world history. The sketches had titles like 'The Dread Redeemer, Lazarus Morell', and 'The Widow Ching, Lady Pirate' or 'The Insulting Master of Etiquette, Kotsuke no Suke.' Borges wrote them for his own entertainment, doing a minimum of research into his subjects and inventing or cooking the facts when it suited him, a trick for which he has subsequently become famous. He wasn't attempting to write history, but to select some details from a colourful figure's life, and the ideas that these gave rise to, and the scenes they enabled him to imagine, and then in five or six pages string these together and bring these characters to life. The material facts of their lives he uses like putty, and he doesn't hide it, speculating on what a character might have thought at a particular moment, effecting rapid scene changes, chopping up the time sequence, and above all presenting the villain's life in a series of brightly-lit scenes.

This is Borges setting the scene for one of his best-known villains.

History (which, like certain film directors, proceeds by a series of abrupt images) now puts forward the image of a danger-filled saloon, located — as if on the high seas — out in the heart of the all-powerful desert. The time, a blustery night of the year 1873; the place, the Staked Plains of New Mexico. All around, the land is almost uncannily flat and bare, but the sky, with its storm-piled clouds and moon, is full of fissured cavities and mountains. There are a cow's skull, the howl and the eyes of coyotes in the shadows, trim horses, and from the saloon an elongated patch of light. Inside, leaning over the bar, a group of strapping but tired men drink a liquor that warms them for a fight; at the same time, they make a great show of large silver coins bearing a serpent and an eagle. A drunk croons to himself, poker-faced. Among the men are several who speak a language with many s's, which must be Spanish, for those who speak it are looked down on. Bill Harrigan, the red-topped tenement rat, stands among the drinkers. He has downed a couple of aguardientes and thinks of asking for one more, maybe because he hasn't a cent left. He is somewhat overwhelmed by these men of the desert. He sees them as imposing, boisterous, happy, and hatefully wise in the handling of wild cattle and big horses. All at once there is dead silence, ignored only by the voice of the drunk, singing out of tune. Someone has come in — a big, burly Mexican, with the face of an old Indian squaw. He is endowed with an immense sombrero and with a pair of six-guns at his side. In awkward English, he wishes a good evening to all the gringo sons of bitches who are drinking. Nobody takes up the challenge. Bill asks who he is, and they whisper to him, in fear, that the Dago — that is, the Diego — is Belisario Villagran, from Chihuahua. At once, there is a resounding blast. Sheltered by that wall of tall men, Bill has fired at the intruder. The glass drops from Villagrans's hand; then the man himself drops. He does not need another bullet. Without deigning to glance at the showy dead man, Bill picks up his end of the conversation. 'Is that so?' he drawled. 'Well, I'm Billy the Kid, from New York.' The drunk goes on singing, unheeded.

Borges comments 'Out of that lucky blast (at the age of fourteen), Billy the Kid the hero was born, and the furtive Bill Harrigan died.' All the tales in this little book have this marvellously strong visual side to them. He also uses bogus 'eye-witness accounts', obituaries, scraps of letters, links with significant historical events, all to give an extraordinary yet light-hearted air of authenticity. He takes chances, but gets away with them.

It's an entertaining and fruitful exercise to flip through a standard encyclopaedia, looking at entries about people, preferably largely unknown to you and the public, decide upon one that interests you, tinker with the facts if you like, throw in a bit of local or historical colour (don't worry if your knowledge of the time and place isn't perfect — think of the New Mexico saloon), select a few scenes you find interesting, and you have your biographical sketch. You'd be advised, however, like Borges, to do it for your own amusement, to flex your muscles in story telling and literary selection, rather than trying to write what blurbs call 'a penetrating study.' But you will be pleased with what you come up with. Obviously it will be better to choose a character who led a fairly exciting life — an explorer, a criminal, a soldier, a prophet.

The entry that follows is the fruit of a five-minute scan through *Everyman's Encyclopaedia* (Vol 6: Norsemen — Precious Stones).

PINKERTON, Allan (1819—84). US detective, born in Glasgow, Scotland. He emigrated to Chicago, where he established the agency which bears his name. He was appointed to the US secret service in 1861, and was prominent in many celebrated cases, assisting in the break-up of the Molly Maguires, a secret society which terrorised the coal districts of Pennsylvania for some 15 years before 1877. Later he was employed as special detective on the great US railways. He published several detective stories, in which his exploits were narrated.

This is the bread and butter of romance. Restless Glaswegian arrives in the New World to find a society perpetually on the edge of anarchy . . . watches a sheriff one day shoot two petty outlaws dead in a bar, only to be shot in the back by another . . . this horrifies the reactionary young man with its waste of resources of law enforcement, which are furthermore so crude that they allow the powers behind crime (which history tells him is bound to become more organised) to escape unnoticed. His Presbyterian (perhaps) background inclines him towards the business élite, who readily supply him with his first contracts. His hatred of the terrorist, Catholic-inspired Molly Maguires leads him on a fifteen year hunt to wipe them out, and the establishment adores him for it. But he has also fallen fatally in love with the imagery of detection, the secrecy and deception and voyeurism, a love which he indulges in his sensational detective stories, in which he shamelessly glamourises his own role. This same love is the cause of his returning to ride the rails across the heart of the lawless American interior, etc, etc, etc.

To make the point once more, this is the Pinkerton of fiction, images and ideas, rather than the Pinkerton of historical fact. I have no idea whether Pinkerton was Presbyterian; but I would certainly enjoy imagining he was, and pulling the threads of the story together on this assumption, and writing scenes which describe the bar room fight, or quoting imaginary extracts from his stories, or describing one journey on the Union Pacific Railway in which Pinkerton in disguise spies on both the passengers and his own detective.

A further encyclopaedia entry, the life of Palissy, an enameller and writer of fantastic stories of 16th century France, appears in the 'Ideas for writing' section which follows.

IDEAS FOR WRITING

Write a brief sketch of someone (you don't as the writer have to be in possession of many facts) by describing some of the pictures in their photographic album.

Describe someone's room in great detail, with a view to letting the reader know what they are like without having yet met them.

Describe someone in terms of their walk, not forgetting that where they are walking, where they might be going, what they are wearing are as important as their physical movements.

Describe a character as seen through the eyes of a child — a favourite uncle, the mother's lover, a teacher, a family friend, a doctor. You don't need to write in the child's language though your observations must be limited to those a child might make, and indirectly using some of the child's words.

You can see, but you cannot hear, two people having a conversation of enormous importance and interest to you. You are watching them from a window, or spying on them from behind a rock. Describe what you see in terms of gestures, movements, facial expressions, and your own guesses about what they *could* be saying.

Describe a person whom you see frequently (along the lines of Ron Barnes's portrait of Willy) on the street, on the bus, at work, and try to bring out a few of their gestures which strike you as typical or strange. Don't pretend to be anything more than an observer of a real person. You don't *know* the character, you've only watched them.

Using the same, or a similar, character, write a brief biography of that person, making up all the details about their childhood, married life, occupation, fears and so on. The novelist H.E. Bates frequently used to do this on trains, only to be alarmed by how accurate his fictional biographies turned out to be when he began talking to his subjects.

'The first time I met Mrs Enderby, she was . . .' Use this as a starting point for a brief portrait of Mrs Enderby, in which you describe a typical action or situation which conveys something essential about her.

In the role of a frequent visitor, describe the essential images of a group of people, such as a family, a group of students sharing a flat, an office, concentrating on the feeling of the group as a whole rather than the individuals in it.

Mime-in-words. Every kind of person smokes a cigarette, takes off a coat, or makes a cup of tea differently from another. Choose one of these actions, and describe three or four kinds of people doing them. No dialogue, only actions.

Finally, a second entry in *Everyman's Encyclopaedia* Vol. 6, (Norsemen — Precious Stones). Use it as a basis for a fictional biography. This is a man with an obsession:

PALISSY, Bernard (c.1510—c.1590). French potter and enameller, born near Agen. His reputation is largely based on literary sources, beginning with his own fantastic writings, according to which he laboured for years in direst poverty to discover how to make fine enamels. Between 1548 and 1563 Palissy succeeded in producing that distinctive ware called by his name, earthenware moulded in high relief with life-like water creatures, shells, fishes, lizards, leaves and other natural objects, and covered with coloured lead-glazes of wonderful harmonies. He escaped the Massacre of St Bartholomew's Day, but with the persecutions of 1586 Palissy was imprisoned in the Bastille, where he died four years later.

5 Doing things with places

Student:	OK, places.
Writer:	Places?
Student:	Yes. How to write about them.
Writer:	Well, it depends what you want to do with them.
Student:	*Do* with them? Why, make them come alive of course, get up off the paper, feel like I'm there, you know.
Writer:	But what about people?
Student:	People? Look, I want to know about places, and you're talking about people. I'll put the people in later. Right now I want some atmosphere. That's the reason I want to know about places. Besides, places are interesting aren't they? You always find writers going on about places — Hardy's Wessex, Dicken's London, Faulkner's —
Writer:	Right. Now let's think about it.

There's a fair amount of thinking to be done. Yes, places are interesting and places in literature equally so, though they are more interesting than the single word atmosphere might suggest. Certainly atmosphere in a story is important. Remember the advertisement for the publisher of romantic fiction which reminds you that love can flourish in ancient castles, sun-drenched beaches or the busy atmosphere of a modern hospital? They know what they're talking about. Not, incidentally, that the atmosphere of a story and its setting are exactly the same. In the story 'Hills Like White Elephants', part of which is quoted on page 36, the atmosphere of stagnation and futility obviously comes more from the nature of the dialogue than from the location. But the setting, of the dusty, deserted train station in central Spain, as the couple wait for a connection certainly contributes to that effect.

The student above certainly would not be alone in finding an enormous appeal in say, Hardy's Wessex, where a geographical area is marvellously recreated from intimate knowledge. But it is

Hardy's sympathy for its inhabitants which gives his knowledge of the countryside such force in his writing. The two are always seen in some kind of relationship. So the student's confident assertion that he'll 'put the people in later' gives cause for alarm. Certainly, pulp romantic or adventure fiction does just that. Thrillers are often set in 'exciting Hong Kong', or New York, or Monte Carlo. Here the atmosphere is just one of the separate ingredients that go to make up the successful formula. The settings could be, often are, switched around without it making much difference. But good writing instinctively recognises the subtle relationships that always exist between people and the places and situations they inhabit, so that this chapter is going to be more about those relationships. Because as the writer says, it depends on what you want to do with them.

Setting the scene

Even the most straightforward use of setting should be more than the frilly ornamentation of the fiction described above. The way in which you write about the place in which your story happens can positively contribute to the mood or ideas of the story itself. Dickens' *Bleak House* concerns a lawsuit which drags on for years, and the lawyers and crooks who profit by it. Dickens begins his novel with a long description of the fog that swirls through the streets of London, then narrows his focus to the Inns of Court:

> The raw afternoon is rawest, and the dense fog is densest, and the muddy streets muddiest, near that leaden-headed old obstruction, appropriate ornament for the threshold of a leaden-headed old corporation: Temple Bar. And hard by Temple Bar, in Lincoln's Inn Hall, at the very heart of the fog, sits the Lord High Chancellor in his High Court of Chancery.

Before the tale even begins to unfold, the reader has a strong sense of gloom and confusion, subsequently strengthened by what happens in the novel.

It is of course possible to bring the relationship between event and place, between what happens and where it happens, even closer so that the setting becomes an important part of the story itself, almost like an extra character. In a story like Ian McEwan's 'Psychopolis,' quoted below, the characters and the setting (Los Angeles) are inseparable. It is a story about barrenness and body-worship and luxury and anxiety and moral decay. The narrator is both attracted and repelled by the city's glamorous-looking boredom:

It was exhilarating, at least at first, to live in a city of narcissists. On my second or third day I followed George's directions and walked to the beach. It was noon. A million stark, primitive figurines lay scattered on the fine, pale, yellow sand till they were swallowed up, north and south, in a haze of heat and pollution. Nothing moved but the sluggish giant waves in the distance, and the silence was awesome. Near where I stood on the very edge of the beach were different kinds of parallel bars, empty and stark, their crude geometry marked by silence. Not even the sound of the waves reached me, no voices, the whole city lay dreaming. As I began walking towards the ocean there were soft murmurs nearby, and it was as if I overheard a sleep-talker. I saw a man move his hand, spreading his fingers more firmly against the sand to catch the sun. An icebox without its lid stood like a gravestone at the head of a prostrate woman. I peeped inside as I passed and saw empty beercans and a packet of orange cheese floating in water. Now that I was moving among them I noticed how far apart each solitary sunbather was. It seemed to take minutes to walk from one to another. A trick of perspective had made me think they were jammed together. I noticed too how beautiful the women were, their brown limbs spread like starfish; and how many healthy old men there were with gnarled muscular bodies. The spectacle of this common intent exhilarated me and for the first time in my life I too urgently wished to be brown-skinned, brown-faced, so that when I smiled my teeth would flash white. I took off my trousers and shirt, spread my towel and lay down on my back thinking, I shall be free, I shall change beyond all recognition. But within minutes I was hot and restless, I longed to open my eyes. I ran into the ocean and swam out to where a few people were treading water and waiting for an especially huge wave to dash them to the shore.

The awful directionless characters in the story are both producers and products of their extraordinary city. The story is about people, there is a plot but it's also about a place, the two existing in inextricable relationship. And because it's about L.A. with its freeways and luxury and sunshine and private houses, it's about an American ideal, and because it's about an American ideal it's about — well, it's about a society rather than just a place.

An Englishman's home

In the chapter 'Writing about people' it was mentioned that one of the ways in which a character can be described is by writing about something which belongs to them, most obviously, of course, their home or their room or their lodgings. Depending on how this is done, it can tell us much that the author wants us to know about their habits, personality, income, social class, taste, marriage, and so on. It is worth remarking that the general habit of lengthy description has declined in writing of this century, partly because prose style in general tends to be more economical, partly also because literature has become more absorbed in psychological reality, at the expense of describing the physical details of a society. Tom Wolfe, the American 'New Journalist', points out that the nineteenth-century novelists always gave the reader plenty of clues as to their characters' position in society, their 'status life.' He quotes Balzac introducing two rather hard-up social climbers, whose status life we can read from:

> The furniture covered in faded cotton velvet, the plaster statuettes masquerading as Florentine bronzes, the clumsily carved painted chandelier with its candle rings of molded glass, the carpet, a bargain whose low price was explained too late by the quantity of cotton in it, which was now visible to the naked eye.

Wolfe goes on to say that this function of minute social categorisation has now been taken over by the so-called New Journalism, which blends fiction and documentary.

It isn't only status life that can be conveyed by the meticulous description of someone's house, but also emotional life — and again we are back to atmosphere, but again it's atmosphere with a purpose. There is a marvellous, lengthy description in Brigid Brophy's novel *Flesh*, of the mock-Tudor suburban mansion owned by the parents of the main character, Marcus, as seen through his eyes. The more we know of Marcus' parents' house, and the smell of furniture polish and the neat 'hostel' bedroom, and 'the terrible pitch of cleanliness at which Marcus' mother kept all fifteen rooms', the more we share the character's sense of oppression in his family home, oppression mixed with a sense of relief at being warm and secure after his dingy flat. Of course, we learn too about his parents' 'status life', about affluent bourgeois mock-Tudor respectability and so on. But it is its emotional reality for Marcus that is the striking thing.

Mental landscape

The Victorian John Ruskin wrote 'All violent feelings . . . produce in us a falseness in all our impressions of external things, which I would generally characterise as the "Pathetic Fallacy" ' — 'pathetic' because it concerns feelings, fallacy because our view of things when we are violently emotional is distorted. A fallacy it may be in strict physiological terms, but as far as writing goes, to link emotion with the world outside is a powerful and much-used way of conveying an emotional state of mind. To give a simple example, a lover's joy is made more real for the reader when set in a beautiful place on a sunny day. The external world is frequently used to reflect the inner world of the individual. In a sense, of course, this is a part of the basic process of writing, using images to show the reader, rather than tell them about, an experience.

In Saul Bellow's first novel, *The Victim*, the hero Leventhal is on his way to an unpleasant meeting:

After a hurried supper of a sandwich and a bottle of soda at a stand near the ferry, Leventhal crossed to Staten Island. He walked onto the deck with his hands in the pockets of his fully buttoned, wrinkled jacket. His white shoes were soiled. Posted beside a life ring, his dark forehead shining faintly under his ill-combed, thick hair, he gazed out on the water with an appearance of composure; he did not look as burdened as he felt. The formless, working, yellowish-green water was dull, the gulls steered back and forth, the boat crept forward into the glare. A barge was spraying orange paint over the hull of a freighter, which pointed high, lifting its bow out of the slow, thick cloud. Surely the sun was no hotter in any Singapore or Surabaya, on the chains, plates, and rails of ships anchored there. A tanker, sea-bound, went across the ferry's course, and Leventhal stared after it, picturing the engine room; it was terrible, he imagined, on a day like this, the men nearly naked in the shaft alley as the huge thing rolled in a sweat of oil, the engines laboring. Each turn must be like a repeated strain on the hearts and ribs of the wipers, there near the keel, beneath the water. The towers on the shore rose up in huge blocks, scorched, smoky, gray, and bare white where the sun was direct upon them. The notion brushed Leventhal's mind that the light over them and over the water was akin to the yellow revealed in the slit of the eye of a wild animal, say a lion, something inhuman that didn't care about anything human and yet was implanted in every human being too, one speck of it, and formed a part of him that responded to the heat and the glare, exhausting as these were, or even to freezing, salty things, harsh things, all things difficult to stand. The Jersey shore, yellow, tawny, and flat, appeared on the right. The Statue of Liberty rose and traveled backwards again; in the trembling air, it was black, a twist of black that stood up like smoke. Stray planks and water-logged, foundering crates washed back in the boat's swell.

Had Leventhal just fallen in love, could he have reacted in the same way to the crossing? Would he have had such sympathy for the men in the shaft alley? Because he is 'burdened' the whole scene strikes him as oppressive, the water is 'formless, working, yellowish-green', the boat 'creeps forward into the glare'. What is surely the most impressive piece of mental landscaping in the passage though is Leventhal's likening of the light on the tower blocks and on the water to 'the yellow revealed in the slit of the eye of a wild animal, say a lion, something inhuman and yet . . . implanted in every human being too'. What a sinister image, and yet how naturally it comes from the Manhattan skyline, filtered through Leventhal's tormented consciousness.

However suggestive of other things this light is, it is still palpably real light on a real river. In H.G. Wells' short story 'The Door In The Wall', a place is described which reveals things about the personality of the main character, but whose existence remains deliberately ambiguous. Wallace, a successful politician talks one night in the club to an old friend, and tells him in some desperation of a secret that has been haunting him since he was a child. When he was about six years old and playing alone he had passed a door in the wall on the street, and felt a strong desire to go in. He had done so and stepped into a garden of unspeakable beauty and 'friendliness'. He had been overwhelmed by the emotion of joy it moved in him.

Circumstances prevent him returning to the garden and when he does try to find it again, he can't. In later life he sees the door in the wall on several occasions, but always at a time when politics are pressing him to move on. 'Who wants to pat panthers on the way to dinner with pretty women and distinguished men?' Finally he realises he has lost something of infinitely greater value to him than the world he has chosen.

Wallace's garden is representative of an inner place which he has destroyed to his cost. It is a symbol of the child-like and innocent in him. Obviously, places can be symbolic of areas of experience. Perhaps the greatest exponent of this technique is Franz Kafka, whose method is to create bizarre or fantastic situations and describe them in matter-of-fact, realistic detail, so that we are wholly convinced of, for example, the reality of his symbolic castle, in the novel of the same name, in which the central character tries repeatedly and unsuccessfully to gain admission; or of the dingy corridors of the law courts in *The Trial* where justice is endlessly talked about, but with no apparent logic or urgency. So real are the places in these novels, despite their evidently metaphoric purpose in the book, that people frequently talk, when describing the oppressiveness of a bureaucratic procedure, of a 'Kafkaesque atmosphere'. And again we are back to our starting point, atmosphere.

The simple point that all these extracts have in common is that while the setting may be important in each, it is always a part of the purpose of the story or sketch as a whole. Places exist in relationship with people. The use a writer makes of place arises from the ideas and emotions of the work itself.

The diagram below may help to bring together in visual form the possible 'uses of place' that have been discussed in this chapter.

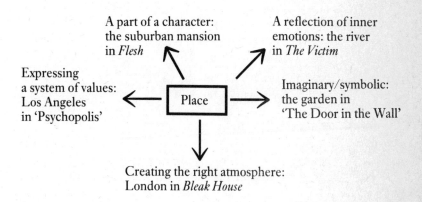

A part of a character: the suburban mansion in *Flesh*

A reflection of inner emotions: the river in *The Victim*

Expressing a system of values: Los Angeles in 'Psychopolis'

Place

Imaginary/symbolic: the garden in 'The Door in the Wall'

Creating the right atmosphere: London in *Bleak House*

6 Who's telling the story?

In writing any piece of fiction, the question of who is to tell the story needs to be thought about. Is it to be you, the author, who knows everything about all the people and all the events in the story? Or is it to be one of your characters, describing what happens to him or her? Are there more ways than just these two to tell a story? The answer to the last question is yes. This chapter looks at the range of possibilities available to you, and the advantages and drawbacks of each.

The three most common ways are:

a) in the third person, where you the writer tell the story
b) in the first person, where the narration is done by one of the characters
c) in the third person, with the focus on one character, from whose point of view the events are related.

The third person   The writer tells the story directly, and does not pretend to be anything other than the teller of the tale. This is how Tolstoy begins *Anna Karenina:*

> All happy families are alike but an unhappy family is unhappy after its own fashion.
> Everything had gone wrong in the Oblonsky household. The wife had found out about her husband's relationship with their former French governess and announced that she could not go on living in the same house with him.

That it is the writer who is telling his readers the story is reinforced by the confident generalisation with which the story opens: 'All happy families . . .'. There is no doubt that the writer is in control. And Tolstoy goes on to tell us in this lengthy novel not only about the Oblonskys, but the Karenins, and Levin and Vronsky, all of whom he can tell us about with the same intimate knowledge.

It is because it is assumed that the author knows everything about his characters that this technique of telling the story is known as that of the 'omniscient author'. At first glance, it may seem that the freer you are the better, so why not go straight for this third person narrative, which puts you in complete control of the characters and the action and which allows you to go anywhere you like? But there is a snag in being the omniscient author, which is that all stories need a focus, and constantly having the responsibility for where you place that focus (the responsibility which is always yours as the omniscient author) can be quite a strain. Put simply, how many of the characters' thoughts and actions are you going to describe and which characters are you going to focus on? The freedom of the third person technique brings with it the need always to make decisions of this kind.

The first person If we look at a different style of narrative technique, writing in the first person, we find different constraints and possibilities. A character in the story (usually, but not always, the main character) speaks to the reader. Here is another opening from a nineteenth century Russian classic, Dostoevsky's *Notes from Underground*:

> I am a sick man . . . I am an angry man. I am an unattractive man. I think there is something wrong with my liver. But I don't understand the least thing about my illness, and I don't know for certain what part of me is affected. I am not having any treatment for it, and never have had, although I have a great respect for medicine, and for doctors. I am besides extremely superstitious, if only in having such respect for medicine. (I am well educated enough not to be superstitious, but superstitious I am.) No, I refuse treatment out of spite.

This is not the writer speaking, but his strange, 'underground man.' The 'focus' is immediately clear, as it is provided by the character who is telling the story. Whereas in third person narrative we have the problem of what to include, and what to leave out, at least with the first person we can only include what our central character has experienced. Simply, he cannot be in two places at once. Nor can he know what other people are thinking, though he can have ideas about it, which may or may not be right. So the path is at least cleared of some choices, in a way that is probably useful to a beginning writer.

The other advantages of the first person technique have already been dealt with in 'Finding a voice' — that the question of the style you write in is made simpler for you because you have to keep to the voice of your narrator, and that this will prevent you from indulging in 'literariness', or at least agonising over the style in which you want to write. It also provides immediacy: this happened to me, I'm telling it to you, which is the most basic form of story telling.

The third person with the focus on a single character   It is the writer who actually tells the story, but he centres it on one character only, so that the story *is* that character's, but the writer can draw back if he wishes, to make a comment or tell the reader about what someone else in the story is doing. In this passage, Arthur, the hero of Alan Sillitoe's *Saturday Night and Sunday Morning* is having a drink with Jack, who is the husband of Brenda, the woman who features in Arthur's thoughts.

Arthur watched him, thankful that certain laws existed to prevent you from seeing into each other's mind, that things were marvellous that way.

'It don't mek no bit o' difference,' the barkeeper insisted, 'not wi' fifty bloody transfers.'

'What about Worrel and Jackson? You can't say they wain't mek any difference.'

Arthur listened in a dreamlike way, happy from the beer he had drunk, dimly remembering the cold earth of the dark wood where he had lain with Brenda, hours ago: he had heard all about football before.

He reflected, fingering what he decided would have to be his last pint if he were not to begin a real bout and fall into a hedgebottom on the way home, that it was just Jack's bad luck. Either you had it in for you, or you didn't. He told himself that he would make the best of it, stack hay while the sun shone. Brenda was a good woman to know, and he wouldn't stop until things cracked up, as they must, he didn't doubt, sometime, one way or another.

Although there is no pretence that anyone other than the writer is telling the story, still the convention is observed that he can only describe what is going on in one character's head, as if, like Arthur, the writer accepted that 'certain laws existed to prevent you from seeing into each other's mind.' In this way, much of the helpful discipline of first-person narrative is retained.

Just how helpful that discipline can be is exemplified by some remarks that E.M. Forster made while writing his novel *A Passage to India*.

> I am bored by the tiresomeness and conventionalities of fiction-form: e.g. the convention that one must view the action through the mind of one of the characters; and say of the others 'perhaps they thought', or at all events adopt their view point for a moment only. If you can pretend you can get inside one character, why not pretend it about all the characters?

But Forster himself immediately supplies the answer to that question:

> 'I see why. The illusion of life may vanish, and the author degenerate into a showman.'

To 'degenerate into a showman' is to treat your characters like puppets, whizzing in and out of everybody's thoughts, rather than limiting your point of view to the partial understanding which is the most any of us can ever have. It is not that writing in the third person must inevitably degenerate into showmanship, simply that the other techniques keep a useful check on you.

Although attention is focused on one character with this narrative mode, and the plot is built around them, the author is free to establish some distance between himself and the character if he so wishes, or even imply criticism. A totally perfect hero or heroine would be a bit of a bore. There can be a range of attitudes towards the main character. Jane Austen described her Emma as 'a heroine whom no one but myself will much like', and while Emma is at root selfish and immature, her wit and liveliness make her attractive to be with. Alan Sillitoe has a certain affection for his Arthur, the hero of *Saturday Night and Sunday Morning*, but shows his insensitivity without hesitation. What we respond to in Arthur is not his morals but his vitality. We enjoy his company. This, too, is part of the 'illusion of life' that good writing has. Writing fiction is much more about creating this illusion than of having a superhuman knowledge of mankind. How you tell your story, or who you tell it through, or who tells it for you, will be a major factor in achieving it.

The best of both worlds?

You may, of course, wish to experiment by using more than one technique at a time, for instance by writing part in the third person and the rest in the first. That does present difficulties in that the 'illusion' is broken. What *is* quite common is to include letters, diary extracts and so on, written by characters in a book which is otherwise told in the third person. This provides the immediacy, and the feeling of objectivity, of the first-hand account, and gives the reader a clear view of a character as they express themselves. The author meanwhile keeps the freedom the third person technique gives him. Or two versions of reality can be played off against each other: John Fowles' *The Collector* is the story of how a repressed, mean, self-pitying young man who has come into a lot of money kidnaps a self-confident and beautiful middle-class girl and keeps her in a specially prepared cellar. The first part of the book is narrated by the young man, the second consists of the diary the girl keeps while she is a prisoner. The interest lies obviously in the relationship between the two views of what is happening.

Or you can write about a character seen through the eyes of another. In the first few pages of Herman Melville's 'Bartleby the Scrivener', a story about a silent, exasperating, sinister petty clerk, the narrator, Bartleby's employer, introduces himself thus:

I am a man who, from his youth upwards, has been filled with a profound conviction that the easiest way of life is the best. Hence, though I belong to a profession proverbially energetic and nervous, even to turbulence, at times, yet nothing of that sort have I ever suffered to invade my peace. I am one of those unambitious lawyers who never addresses a jury, or in any way draws down public applause; but, in the cool tranquillity of a snug retreat, do a snug business among rich men's bonds, and mortgages, and title-deeds. All who know me, consider me an eminently safe man. The late John Jacob Astor, a personage little given to poetic enthusiasm, had no hesitation in pronouncing my first grand point to be prudence; my next, method. I do not speak it in vanity, but simply record the fact, that I was not unemployed in my profession by the late John Jacob Astor; a name which, I admit, I love to repeat; for it hath a rounded and orbicular sound to it, and rings like unto bullion. I will freely add, that I was not insensible to the late John Jacob Astor's good opinion.

We form the impression of a man who is complacent, pompous and perfectly satisfied with the world and himself. The reader is bound to ask how far such a person can be trusted to understand the tortured, enigmatic soul of Bartleby.

Representing another variation on 'straight' narration, many of Henry James' short stories concern events which are narrated by people at three or four removes from the events themselves, via people who have their own ideas about the significance of those events. Whose is the right story? Nobody's. It's the spaces between that matter most. Paul Scott does this over a vast area in his *Raj Quartet*, set in India, in which an unspecified shadowy narrator strings together a story with diary entries, conversations with people twenty years after the event, official memoranda, club registers, unpublished memoirs, letters, reminiscences and so on to build up a vastly complicated picture of India around the time of independence.

In the next chapter, a short piece of work by a student who tinkers with the question of who is telling the story is examined in detail.

IDEAS FOR WRITING

Write a possible opening scene for a short story, in which, say, someone is waiting to meet their estranged wife or husband, in two ways: in the third person, with you the writer describing whatever you think important to the scene, and then in the first person, so that we have only your own thoughts as you wait.

A short story in letters only — letters to and from, say, four or five people, allowing the plot to develop through the

71

letters. Some possible situations: a soldier abroad writes home, but he is changing, and so is home; an administrative error in a big hospital leads to a baby being given to the wrong mother, with complicated consequences, including a possible cover-up attempt; letters to a problem page, the internal memos that circulate round the magazine office, a mistake or two, and the printed replies.

A short story in which it emerges that your narrator does not fully understand what is going on in the story, because he has misunderstood something said to him, or because he lacks the sensitivity to see what is really happening.

You recall an important scene in your family history (a death, an unpopular marriage, a large and unexpected gift of money), which took place when you were an adolescent. Compare your impression of this with a diary which you then find in the loft, in which the writer (grandparent, sister, cousin, brother-in-law) describes that event in detail as it was happening. It could, of course, also be your own diary that you find.

Write the opening scene of a story in which a character is talking about an experience they have had. Try to make the reader gradually aware that you do not necessarily share your character's views — but remember that they are doing all the talking. (See also 'Finding a voice': the stories 'Spiv in Love' and 'You Should Have Seen the Mess').

This is the beginning of Edgar Allan Poe's classic horror story 'The Tell-tale Heart';

TRUE! — nervous — very, very dreadfully nervous I had been and am; but why will you say that I am mad? The disease had sharpened my senses — not destroyed — not dulled them. Above all was the sense of hearing acute. I heard all things in the heaven and in the earth. I heard many things in hell. How, then, am I mad? Hearken! and observe how healthily — how calmly I can tell you the whole story.

It is impossible to say how first the idea entered my brain; but once conceived, it haunted me day and night. Object there was none. Passion there was none. I loved the old man. He had never wronged me. He had never given me insult. For his gold I had no desire. I think it was his eye! yes, it was this! He had the eye of a vulture — a pale blue eye, with a film over it. Whenever it fell upon me, my blood ran cold; and so by degrees — very gradually — I made up my mind to take the life of the old man, and thus rid myself of the eye forever.

It is evident that he *is* a madman, despite his protestations. Write a story in which the narrator is disturbed in some way, so that we are never entirely sure of the 'truth' of what he is saying.

7 Who's telling the story — second time around

This chapter looks at one very short story in the making. The story does raise some questions about 'point of view' — but with all kinds of creative writing, it is impossible to talk about a piece only in terms of one aspect. The story, written by a student, is interesting for other reasons, such as the style the writer uses and the revisions she makes after the first draft.

A story that tells of a relationship between two people, particularly of a sexual or emotional kind, where sometimes it can be hard to tell where one person stops and the other begins, provides a useful starting point for examining narrative viewpoint or angle. You can devote a whole book to it, as John Fowles does in *The Collector*, or you can try and tackle it in a sketch as the student does here. Can there be such a thing as the correct view of a relationship? Should you just concentrate on one side? But then what about the other partner? Don't they get a look in? Perhaps you could let one of them describe the whole thing, but make it clear that you sympathise with the other (as in 'Spiv in Love' quoted in 'Finding a voice').

In the story below, about a husband and wife, the writer uses the common third person narration with the focus on one character, referring to the husband as 'he' but viewing the relationship through only his eyes. We learn in two ways about the couple, through the husband's thoughts and through the dialogue. What do we learn about the wife, and how?

'Funeral' (First draft)

'The woman has died in me,' he thought.
'And now her corpse pleads for our sake . . .'
Soon the gold would bite his guilt.

He hated fuss at funerals. He knew this would go on and on and on.

'Why don't you tell me if there is another woman?' 'I'll understand.'

'You can make .me understand.' 'But please don't, you musn't . . .'

He knew he wasn't expected to speak or explain. Only listen and feel sorry. For her?

'But what went wrong? Tell me that at least! I didn't even know you were thinking all these things, all this while. Talk to me!'

He thought of the ultimate in road signs. Stop. Finish explanations. Proceed.

'I'm fed up of railway compartments,' he began quietly.

'But what's that got to do with our marriage?'

'I'm entitled to leave and travel allowance. And maternity leave for my wife. I drink coffee from a pot in the office. At home I make do with a mug.'

His eyes were fixed on her tee-shirt. He needn't look at her face to read her. The tee-shirt revealed all. Right now it flashed, 'Stop confusing me you bastard.'

'Talk sense will you? We've been married two and a half years. And now all you can talk of is trains and maternity money.'

If he weren't so drained already he'd have gone across and hugged her. He wasn't sure how she'd interpret that.

'Do you want me to go to my mother's for a few days? I know I can get on your nerves sometimes. I can always manage to go to work from there.'

Toss. Grope. Catch. The quick-and-easy century.

He thought of solutions in cans and test-tube tomorrows when he made love to her that night.

Next morning she felt alright.

'Why had he made love to her?' he asked himself.

No, he didn't regret it. As always he felt good about it. He couldn't figure out why. 'I have rejected her, haven't I? Am I using her?

Or . . . am I paying back a debt? What debt?'

No use denying he didn't feel guilty about all this. But this way, this could go on endlessly. 'How do I bury the corpse with the minimum of ceremony?'

She thought of last night. 'Yes it's all over. The trouble has blown over.' Her confidence made her a woman again.

'Have you checked the alarm?' she asked him after dinner next night.

'I didn't hear it ring this morning. About last night . . . I want to . . .'

'Forget last night.'

'I just wanted to say how . . .'

'Cut the symbolism from last night. There wasn't any.' He knew what she was fumbling over . . . How can a marriage die without explanations?

He wondered if he were the corpse himself. Would it be easier burying him?

He thought of his managing director's secretary. She was leaving after 23 years with the company. There wasn't a single typewriter in the whole office she hadn't used and passed on to the newcomers.

Who is she? Does she know? She's all glass and reflection. Too dazzling for comfort. Too expensive for day-to-day consumption. My wife.

Scratch me out of yourself, wife. Do it now. Or you'll be dead.

The husband's impressions (he is an interesting analyst of his own feelings: 'Toss. Grope. Catch. The quick and easy century') contrast with his inarticulate complaints, and his wife's helpful suggestions ('Do you want me to go to my mother's for a few days?'). But when we get to the sentence half way through 'The next morning she felt alright', we face a problem. Is this something being told us through the husband's consciousness?. Is that just what he thought? If so, nothing has changed. But soon we read 'She too thought of last night. 'Yes it's all over. The trouble has blown over.' Her confidence made her a woman again.' This strikes the reader as puzzling because it is inconsistent. So far the writer has concentrated on the man's perceptions — now we are let into the woman's mind. But only for a moment. Back to the man, up to the final 'Scratch me out of yourself, wife.' It is as if the door has suddenly been opened on to the wife and then slammed shut. Better to have left it locked, and let the reader enjoy speculating about what was behind it. What's more, that brief reaction, 'The trouble has blown over', because they made love the previous night, is a rather stereotyped one, and the woman instead of remaining simply unknown to us, becomes a stereotype too.

A diagram might illustrate the problem. Everything inside the triangle is the story:

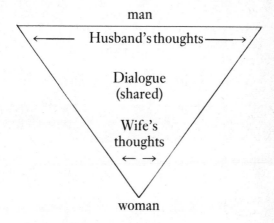

man

Husband's thoughts

Dialogue
(shared)

Wife's
thoughts

woman

The imbalance is obvious: if we are to know *any* of the wife's thoughts, let us know them all, or we will feel the full side of her story has been withheld. Alternatively, let us know only the man's, and be left to work out the woman for ourselves.

The criticism was made, the writer thought about it. In the next version she looks at her first draft again before moving on to the second, and finds much she wants to change, and cut:

'Funeral' (First draft, with student's comments)

'The woman has died in me,' he thought.
'And now her corpse pleads for our sake . . .
~~Soon the gold would bite his guilt.~~   arty
He hated fuss at funerals. He knew this would go on and on and on.

77

'Why don't you tell me if there is another woman?' 'I'll understand.'

'You can make me understand.' 'But please don't, you musn't . . .'

adds ~~He knew he wasn't expected to speak or explain. Only~~
nothing ~~listen and feel sorry. For her?~~

~~'But what went wrong? Tell me that at least! I didn't even~~
~~know you were thinking all these things, all this while. Talk~~
~~to me!'~~

He thought of the ultimate in road signs. Stop. Finish explanations. Proceed.

revise {
'I'm fed up of railway compartments,' he began quietly.

'But what's that got to do with our marriage?'

'I'm entitled to leave and travel allowance. And maternity leave for my wife. I drink coffee from a pot in the office. At home I make do with a mug.'
}

all too ~~His eyes were fixed on her tee-shirt. He needn't look at her~~
'clever' ~~face to read her. The tee-shirt revealed all. Right now it~~
~~flashed, 'Stop confusing me you bastard.'~~

~~'Talk sense will you? We've been married two and a half~~
~~years. And now all you can talk of is trains and maternity~~
~~money.'~~

complicates ~~If he weren't so drained already he'd have gone across and~~
things ~~hugged her. He wasn't sure how she'd interpret that.~~

too 'Do you want me to go to my mother's for a few days? +
obvious ~~I know I can get on your nerves sometimes.~~ I can always manage to go to work from there.'

Toss. Grope. Catch. The quick-and-easy century.

too He thought of solutions in cans and test-tube tomorrows
arty when he made love to her that night. / *more about the woman here ??*

Next morning she felt alright.

irrelevant ~~'Why had he made love to her?' he asked himself.~~
~~No, he didn't regret it. As always he felt good about it. He~~
~~couldn't figure out why. 'I have rejected her, haven't I? Am~~
~~I using her?~~
~~Or . . . am I paying back a debt? What debt?'~~

~~No use denying he didn't feel guilty about all this. But this way, this could go on endlessly. 'How do I bury the corpse with the minimum of ceremony?'~~

She thought of last night. 'Yes it's all over. The trouble has blown over.' Her confidence made her a woman again. *expand*

put later ➔ 'Have you checked the alarm?' she asked him after dinner next night.

'I didn't hear it ring this morning. About last night . . . I want to . . .'

~~'Forget last night.'~~

~~'I just wanted to say how . . .'~~

YUK! ~~'Cut the symbolism from last night. There wasn't any.' He knew what she was fumbling over . . . How can a marriage die without explanations?~~

pushing the funeral idea a bit far? He wondered if he were the corpse himself. Would it be easier burying him?

He thought of his managing director's secretary. She was leaving after 23 years with the company. There wasn't a single typewriter in the whole office she hadn't used and passed on to the newcomers.

too slick! ~~Who is she? Does she know? She's all glass and reflection. Too dazzling for comfort. Too expensive for day-to-day consumption. My wife.~~

weak ending ~~Scratch me out of yourself, wife. Do it now. Or you'll be dead.~~

Another conversation needed - about going to the pictures? The woman is too shadowy in the story - or should she be out of it altogether? She is a stereotype, tho'. That's why the hub. is fed up with her. The conversation, and some of her thoughts, could show that, maybe.

She has cut a great deal; significantly, and quite rightly, it is the slick, self-conscious writing that goes first: 'Too expensive for day to day comfort. My wife.' Some of the shakier dialogue is cut, too: the rambling about coffee in pots or mugs and maternity leave, and the American B-movie-type 'Cut the symbolism from last night. There wasn't any.' A few notes are made, that what we know of the wife is unsatisfactorily told. The problem is that the wife is meant to be a 'stereotype' of a woman anyway. 'That's why the hub. is fed up with her,' the writer notes. She wonders how to make this clear. The fruits of her painstaking approach, and her willingness to cut a large proportion on her own initiative, are shown in the second, final draft.

Funeral (Final draft)

'The woman has died in me,' he thought.
And now her corpse pleads 'for our sake . . .'

He hated fuss at funerals. He knew somehow that this one would go on and on and on.

'Why don't you tell me if there is another woman? I'll understand. I can help. You can get over it. After all a marriage is stronger than any other woman, isn't it?'

He thought of the ultimate in road signs. Stop. Finish explanations. Proceed.

'I'm fed up of railway compartments.' He began quietly. 'I'm bothered about the way I can make you do just about anything.'

'But that's surely not a crisis. Tell me what's wrong. Can't you talk seriously. Do you want me to go to my mother's for a few days? I can get to work from there. You can have dinner next door.'

Toss. Grope. Catch. The quick and easy century. He thought of solutions in cans and 'hit and miss marriages' when he made love to her that night.

Why did he do that? There's somebody who has been sleeping next to me for two years. She happens to be my wife. Is that a good enough reason? I'm not even sure what makes her tick. What she feels deep inside, whether she knows she has an inside. And I say I don't care . . . then why?

She thought things were okay next morning. His silence was unnerving. But she let it pass. She planned on buying tickets for the evening show and then calling him at her office. An evening out would do him good, she thought.

'I'm married,' he kept telling himself in between his memos, and letters and phone calls and coffee.

I have a ready made wife. A company flat. A credit card. And still the blank wall day after day.

He didn't mean to be offensive when he asked her to go to the movie by herself.

She was home before him. The tea was ready.

'You wanted me to go for a six o'clock show alone? Did you figure out how I would get back? What if somebody saw me leaving the theatre alone? I could get picked up you know. Do you ever wonder what it is like to be a woman?'

He wondered if she knew. He wondered if her mother knew. Or his mother for that matter. He wondered what they felt when they got their periods every month. He had asked her once and she had stared at him.

He kept thinking of his secretary. She was leaving after 23 years with the company. There wasn't a single typewriter in the whole office she hadn't used and passed on to newcomers. He wondered what typewriters felt staying in the place so long.

'We have to go next door for dinner tomorrow. It's the little one's birthday. Should we take a present?'

'You decide.'

'I think we'll buy him a shirt. Blue suits him fine. Don't forget to check the alarm. I don't think I heard it ring this morning.'

He wondered if he were the corpse himself.

Should he start believing in life after death?

She has kept the best of the husband's enigmatic thoughts — cricket, road signs, typewriters. The story has been tightened up, and the melodrama of 'Stop confusing me you bastard' or 'Am I using her? Or . . . am I paying back a debt? What debt?' gives way to something bleaker — the incomprehension about periods and the time he had asked her, the apathy of 'He wondered what typewriters felt staying in the place so long.' But rather than eliminate the thoughts of the wife she has increased them. She tells us not only that the wife was relieved the morning after love-making, but that she had plans to improve the relationship by organising a trip to the cinema. The proportion of dialogue to the man's thoughts is increased too, so that we learn more about her that way too. But the story remains the husband's. It is *his* thoughts that are interesting, his language that is special. The wife occupies a bigger area of the triangle, but the imbalance is still there. Critics talk in elaborate ways about 'artistic structure', but it often comes down to something like this — a feeling of proportion. Either a story such as this is about 'a relationship seen from the husband's point of view' with dialogue to complement that, or it is a view of both sides, as in *The Collector*, where the space between the two people's versions is of enormous importance. 'Funeral' doesn't quite manage to avoid falling between these two stools.

It should be said at some stage that for the story really to take off, it should be rather longer so that our knowledge of the relationship is deepened. As it stands, though, it succeeds quite well in capturing a mood, of bleakness and apathy. The solution of our immediate problem is not hard to see. If the paragraph which begins 'She thought things were okay next morning' were cut out altogether, then the wife would remain 'unknown' to us. We know about the husband, we know about the dialogue, what is going on in the wife's mind is up to us to guess. And — this is both one of the pleasures and one of the fundamental principles of creative writing — there don't have to be any right answers. In 'Funeral' we know all that it is generally given to one person to know in reality. And that makes for 'the illusion of life'.

8 The world from the inside

Follow your thoughts

At the end of the chapter 'Finding a voice', about writing
monologues, it was clear that we were moving away from
anything simply definable as a character sketch, or a story told
by one person, and towards something I called then a 'meditation'. In this, an intensely private world was being created, with
its own private images and rhythms, suggesting an individual
consciousness relating to what is immediately around it. If you
are writing a story you are bound to some extent by the need to
get your plot moving — even though an enormous amount of
your plot may spring from the development of a character. But if
you are interested in short, experimental pieces, you may not be
so interested in plot, or even in character. You may want to push
language to the limits you can take it, in an effort to explore that
mysterious personal world we all inhabit, but which the
demands of social living rarely allow us to communicate. You sit
looking out of the window, or lean against a bus stop in the
queue, or let your attention wander as someone speaks to you, or
watch the pattern the streetlamps make on the cement. Instead
of forcing yourself back to 'reality', you follow your thoughts for
a few minutes.

This meditation simply takes a feeling as its starting point, a
feeling that something is about to happen.

'Emergence'

Yesterday I felt something straining inside me. The
dream that had lain so passive in its womb was outgrowing
it. And I felt the strain.

There is this tree I've always seen. It's beyond the
neighbour's wall. Sitting upon it, the other day, I happened
to notice how the root had insidiously crept half into the
wall. Now every day I hold my breath and look out for the
ultimate shattering of plaster that will leave the bricks bare,
exposed. The wall is tense.

I've felt the frantic convulsions of the earth as the sun tries to push itself out, and seen it bursting at the seams . . . and held my breath. And the cloud, I can hear its lining slowly being ripped open, and wait . . . for the stitches of rain to fall apart.

Looking at the sea, a blue ache in the distant afternoon sun, always makes my eyes seem blue too. Achingly blue. So blue that they could be the eyes of the sea. And the ache inside them, the ache of the sea — so deep that the sea walks with me. On the road. And sees — the man and the woman on my left and right walk beside me. The man with his left foot first, the woman with her right. And me, I can't really decide. It's difficult whichever way I do, we're not going to be together all of us. I'd like it. It looks good, feels good. To have rhythm. I try to have it. Keep shuffling. And reshuffling. Finally it works.

I have this weight on me. It's massive. But I feel like the mountain — its shoulders sagging under the weight of clouds.

You see, I must, I have to rhyme with everything, and everything, just everything has to rhyme with me. Like when I write this, the skin on my knuckles flexes to jerk my fingers up and down and the letters emerge. Even a scrawl is rhythmic! Rhyming with the dream.

Now out, grown, emerged, rhymed. This.

When first she read this to a group of fellow students, the response was a request to hear it again. And then again. Even then, several people criticised it because they felt baffled. And it did prove impossible to paraphrase. But that could be something in its favour: if it were paraphrasable, if it could simply be 'put into other words', then the unique private quality of the piece would be lost. It is the essence of private experience that it resists this process — which isn't to say that it can't be communicated. It is true that she uses words in an idiosyncratic way: 'Looking at the sea, a blue ache in the distant afternoon sun, always makes my eyes seem blue too'. But the sensual image is a powerful one. There is a strong sense, too, of the private consciousness actually altering the physical world in 'And the cloud, I can hear its lining slowly being ripped open, and wait . . . for the stitches of rain to fall apart.'

Another person objected to the incoherence of the thoughts. What was the connection between the various observations, between the wall, the sea, walking in step, having to rhyme, and writing itself? This is not an easy criticism to answer. The central idea, as the title suggests, is one of emergence, an intensely personal awareness of something about to happen, and this binds the first three paragraphs together. The next section, about rhythm and walking in step, loses that sense — which returns, in a baffling conjunction with the idea of rhythm, in the final two paragraphs.

On the plus side, however, its casual tone perfectly fits the elusive thought processes. She seems naturally to think in metaphor and images. At each new reading it keeps its spontaneity — it's a meditation, not an essay. An essay looks at a topic in a public way, and so has to be clearly understood. A meditation explores more private thoughts and feelings. In this sense it's 'writing from the inside'.

The term 'meditation' was first used in this way by Franz Kafka, in an early collection of one page or half page prose pieces to which he gave the general title *Meditations*. Nor was there anything new about a young writer producing brief sketches of this sort. Writers have always drafted short pieces which they can later incorporate, if they choose, into longer works. As a young man James Joyce coined the term 'epiphany' (literally, a 'showing forth'), for his descriptions of intense moments of a very personal nature — personal not in the common sense of private and therefore embarrassing, but rather, dealing with the kind of experience unique to the closed world of the individual. Joyce used several of these later in *A Portrait of the Artist as a Young Man*. There is a famous one when the young hero, based on Joyce himself, sees a young girl on the seashore whom he describes in an intense and poetic way in terms of a swan. Kafka, however, published his *Meditations* to be read on their own. Like Joyce (and both of them introduced this essentially modern element into literature) Kafka was concerned with the sometimes oppressive quality of the individual's private experience. For Kafka at least, it could produce an almost imprisoning sense of anxiety, something which later twentieth century writing is full of. Kafka's have titles like 'The Street Window', 'Passers-by', 'On a Tram', even 'The Wish to be a Red Indian'.

Inside somebody else's world

If your own private world doesn't seem to offer the right scope, try somebody else's. This next piece shows yet another interpretation, entering the fictional private world of a real public figure. You may be able to guess for yourself which prominent politician the student who wrote this had in mind.

'An eastern story'

I live in a big house in a part of the world called The East. I am a child. People say that I am a man. I think it's the same thing. I am a man-child.

I am excited. I have been given a whole new toy-set. There are no pieces missing. I open it in the middle of the nursery. Millions of statuettes surround me. They are pawns I can play with. I set them all up.

I have been told I have strong and piercing eyes. These eyes do not like what they see. I kick out at a row of soldiers. They spray out from under my feet and lie scattered, broken. I shall bestow my favours on this statue, and this one. They are my generals, my spokesmen.

I am the Lord.

Lord? Don't say the word aloud. There was a rich man-child living in this house before me. People called him The Prince. He used to play, the same game. He used to call himself 'Lord'. And one day he fell down and hurt himself so badly that he has to beg for help now. His money is of no more use to him.

But I am clever. I will not make the same mistake. I will assume a guise. The robe of a priest. A long and flowing beard.

I am safe now. My mantle of religion is protective. It gives me strength and confidence. Walking back to the middle of the room, I kick some more statues. They fall and be still. That is good. I am in full control. The remaining toys shall form a tight circle around me.

I am invincible.

I can do anything.

And the neighbours shake their fists at me from the other side of the fence. I am too clever for you. You cannot pin anything onto me.

I continue playing with my toys. I knock them over, one by one.

The days pass.

There are few left standing now. I will set them all up again. I try. They fall. I try again. And again. It was a game then. Now, it has become an obsession.

In quiet desperation I try and make my toys stand. My desperation turns to fear. I panic. I rush out of the nursery and hear my voice echo down the corridors . . . Nanny . . . Nanny . . . help me.

I run, I slip, I fall. My beard falls off, my holy garments are torn. There is no one to save me. I have to help myself.

For people call me the man-child.

While it has many of the qualities of any insecure megalomaniac, the specific character the student is entering into is the Ayatollah Khomeini. Obviously, much of the grotesque effect comes from placing him in a nursery lining up his toy soldiers, so that there is something pleasantly chilling about 'I rush out of the nursery and hear my voice echo down the corridors.' How cut off from reality *is* this hugely powerful character?

Now we are almost back where we were at the end of 'Finding a voice', with the private world of a created character, in a monologue. But there is a slight difference: whereas a monologue generally is concerned with a character and his ideas about things, a meditation is more about feelings, about a very private sort of world. And what we have with 'An eastern story' is not a realistic portrait of the Ayatollah, but a way in to his private world . . . his world from the inside.

It may be that you have found one of these kinds of writing more interesting than the others, and will try one yourself. Private images, rather than public ideas, are the key.

Finally, a look at two short meditations by Franz Kafka.

'Passers-by'

When you go walking by night up a street and a man, visible a long way off — for the street mounts uphill and there is a full moon — comes running towards you, well, you don't catch hold of him, not even if he is a feeble and ragged creature, not even if someone chases yelling at his heels, but you let him run on.

For it is night, and you can't help it if the street goes uphill before you in the moonlight, and besides, these two have maybe started that chase to amuse themselves, or perhaps they are both chasing a third, perhaps the first is an innocent man and the second wants to murder him and you would become an accessory, perhaps they don't know anything about each other and are merely running separately home to bed, perhaps they are night birds, perhaps the first man is armed.

And anyhow, haven't you a right to be tired, haven't you been drinking a lot of wine? You're thankful that the second man is now long out of sight.

Here is that sense of anxiety, of indecision, I mentioned earlier. But what is extraordinary about it is the uncertainty of the 'context' of the piece. It begins apparently as a general consideration of what you do when somebody tears past you in the street at night, then it slides into nervous internal speculations about what these two 'imaginary' people were in fact up to, as the speaker defensively answers an imaginary charge of inaction, and finishes with a vivid, alarming sense of the present: 'You're thankful that the second man is now long out of sight.' A generalised worry becomes, in three short paragraphs, an extremely unsettling specific event. Kafka pulls off this trick again, even more deftly, in this last one. A single sentence takes us in a long breath through the development of a fantasy, the yearning for release in speed and motion. Release from what, isn't specified; but the *sense* of it is powerful in the images.

'The Wish to be a Red Indian'

If one were only an Indian, instantly alert, and on a racing horse, leaning against the wind, kept on quivering jerkily over the quivering ground, until one shed one's spurs, for there needed no spurs, threw away the reins, for there needed no reins, and hardly saw that the land before one was smoothly shorn heath when horse's neck and head would be already gone.

9 'A proper story'

Student: Look, this is all very well, but I want to know how to write proper stories.

Writer: Sorry, 'how to write' isn't allowed —

Student: OK, 'about writing'

Writer: — and what are 'proper stories?'

Student: You know ... Oh, I've read about monologues and dialogues and first and third person narrative, and meditations and epiphanies and God knows what, but what about stories, you know, with a beginning, a middle, and an end. Where something *happens* instead of just being ... *meditated* upon.

Writer: Like you read in magazines and anthologies?

Student: Exactly.

Writer: And with a plot?

Student: Yes, yes, with a plot! So that at the end the reader shuts the book with a snap and a satisfied look on his face, and says '*That* was a good story!'

Writer: How about if he's smiling and shaking his head, or thinking again about what he's just read and not feeling sure about it, or staring ahead in horror at the blank wall in front of him?

Student: That'll do, too.

Writer: Because whereas a *novel* generally gives you the feeling of everything having been sorted out ...

Student: When the hero's chased the heroine for 300 pages and finally they're getting married ...

Writer: Right ...

Student: When the heroine finally realises in the seventeenth chapter that she's no longer a girl, but a young woman now?

Writer: And —

Student: — and when the railway finally reaches the town and with it brings the end of an era and the lives of its inhabitants will never be the same again?

Writer: Quite. Whereas in a short story . . .

Student: In a short story we're not concerned with following people over a period of time and watching them changing, moving towards something. It's more like . . . like a stone being thrown into a pool and the reader being left at the end watching the ripples expand?

Writer: Well, yes . . .

Student: So it's more likely to be an incident than a series of events. A dramatic incident that tells you something. Teaches you about life . . . which a novel can't do because you get all bogged down in psychology and realism and meditations and stuff.

Writer: Er, now hold on . . .

Student: Yes, I get it. One incident — POW! Leave 'em reeling, thinking about things. OK, right. Gimme a pen.

Hand over the formula!

Well, some progress has been made in one area at least — the differentiation between a novel and a short story. Each is suited to different things. Whereas in a novel we generally find a whole landscape, hills, valleys, plains, mountains, with a range of emotions and ideas of differing degrees of intensity and importance, in a short story we generally find the writer dealing with one emotion, one incident, one climax, a central idea. If the novel gives us hills and valleys, the short story takes us to a peak, and leaves us there. So that when writing a short story, attempting to handle too much can be a danger. Edgar Allan Poe, one of the 'founders' of the short story form, laid down in 1842 that a short story should aim for 'a single effect', a 'unity of impression.' And while there are some short stories which aim for more than this, as a working rule it's still a good one. It wasn't long after this that a 'moment of crisis' was judged to be essential, in which that single effect could most powerfully manifest itself. This is rather more problematic. Many stories, certainly, deal with a moment of crisis in someone's life when, our student would be glad to see, they learn something about themselves or other people; but there are also many masters of the short story who have developed a low-key approach to the form, so that their stories are more like a glimpse or a snapshot of a situation, in which the characters' 'crisis' may be ill-defined and from which they may not learn anything at all.

The student's claim to have cracked the secret of short story writing is obviously suspect, as anybody's claim would be. There are no secrets to be cracked in writing, and the student has seized upon one kind of short story, that which deals with a single dramatic incident, and is carrying it off in triumph, having found the formula. The idea that any good short story can be written to a formula has to be rejected. It might have seemed sensible to start categorising different *kinds* of short story (the crime story, the love story, the sci-fi story, the western story, the horror story and so on), and seeing what possibilities each one offered. But that would lead us straight into formula: every crime story must have a body, a motive, a detective, a hitch in the detection process, etc. A formula is easy to follow, a good story is hard to write.

This is not to deny that hundreds of short stories are written specifically to a formula every month, and published. The staff of teenage and romance and sci-fi and horror and mystery magazines regularly turn out short stories in which the basic ingredients are endlessly rearranged to produce the stories their readers want. The fiction editor of True Teenage Romance (for example) might draw up a list along these lines:

1 Handsome doctor trying to get over beautiful wife's death in car accident.
2 Successful dancer discovers she has contracted crippling disease.
3 Exclusive Club Mediterranné type chalet village in Tenerife.
4 Bullying business-man husband of dancer in search of his run-away wife.
5 Telegram found lying on hotel bed, after fabulous day exploring local sights, beginning REGRET HUSBAND/ WIFE/FRIEND KILLED IN PLANE CRASH STOP.

Five minutes' work to draw up the list, another three to decide the order in which they are to go, and then pass it on to a sub-editor to flesh it out.

A characteristic of the finished product is that there will be nothing original, nothing fresh, about the situations in the story or the way in which they are handled, nor will the characters be anything more than cardboard cutouts wheeled around the story to keep the plot running on its predictable course. Any reader worth writing for will be bored by such repetition of recognisable formulae. Life itself and the relationships between people do not follow such set patterns, (nor in this case could the initial situation be described as anything other than artificially 'glamorous'). So we will leave *categories* of short story alone, and assume that we can talk about 'the short story', where people and the situations in which they find themselves are recognised as being important.

The distinction should be made before we move on between formula writing (as above), and the conscious use of devices or situations which have been used before. There is no need to set a precedent every time you think of a plot. The so-called eternal triangle, where A loves B who loves C, who may well love A, is a situation rich in dramatic potential that writers have always exploited, and will continue to do so. It looks, as a matter of fact, as if our fictitious fiction editor is heading that way too. Obviously, the success of a story depends upon the way it is handled. The cynicism in the editor's approach of knocking together basic ingredients is guaranteed to keep the finished product well within the limits of the formula story.

A full stop, or a straggle of dots?

To return to our student: it is to be hoped that all that stuff about monologues and dialogues will be seen to have relevance to all creative writing, including proper stories. Short stories have to be well written like everything else, their form has to be thought about, their settings have to be quite familiar in some way to the writer, and all the rest of it. Most of the different aspects of writing so far discussed will come together in different ways in any short story. The finished product that the student is after is the putting together of all these things. So is there anything about the finished product which is different from other literary forms?

One — singleness of effect — has already been mentioned. It is also significant that the student puts his finger on the *structure* of the short story: 'with a beginning, a middle and an end.' His point is a fair one. He's had enough of sketches. It's true that in most short stories tangible events happen and are felt to be leading to some sort of conclusion, so that we always want to know what happens next, unlike in, say, a sketch where something is being thought about or described. As one respected practitioner of the short story, Somerset Maugham, said, 'I preferred to end my stories with a full stop rather than a straggle of dots.' That's the way he liked to write. In his short story 'The Outstation', an isolated colonial of the old school is joined at his remote post in the jungle by an 'upstart', a company worker from a different social class. The old colonial is so incensed by the new man's boorish behaviour and indifference to custom (both native and colonial) that he finally contrives to murder him. End of conflict, end of story. A dramatic incident from its cause to its conclusion. The book snaps shut, the customer is satisfied.

Clearly-drawn characters, a strong story line and a satisfying conclusion appeal to many writers and readers. Bill Naughton, one of Britain's most popular short story writers, locates his stories firmly in a well-defined social setting, usually the North of his early life, exploits his intimacy with local speech to give his stories vitality and a strong realistic feel, and generally builds his stories round one incident of a dramatic or humorous nature. In 'Seeing a Beauty Queen Home', a young man, who obviously fancies himself with women, escorts a girl back to her grandmother's house late at night. The girl pretends to her gran upstairs that she is alone, but the old lady soon comes down to see for herself. Quick as a flash, the young man hits upon the idea of pretending to be a neighbour's son who has of course grown up a bit since she last saw him. He exploits the old lady's failing eyesight and the dim light, and his quick-wittedness pulls him through the interrogation. When the couple are left alone, he turns to the girl in triumph. She responds however by kicking him out of the house, disgusted by his skill at impersonation which to her suggests long practice. The table turned on the crafty hero, the story ends.

Such stories are the literary equivalents of anecdotes, or yarns recounted in the pub, or well-told jokes that build up nicely and have a satisfying punch line. As with such jokes, tell the plot before the story is read and the enjoyment is ruined. It's a kind of story telling that hasn't changed much since Chaucer's day, and in fact the device of a false identity is one that Chaucer himself used frequently.

But even Chaucer didn't always end his stories off with a full stop and a sound punch line. Not every reader likes things so neatly sewn up. The ripples of such a story, to use the student's metaphor, don't continue to issue from its centre. And the ability to produce continuous ripples is one of the short story's potential strengths, and one which many of the great short story writers exploit. In other words, they end their stories with a straggle of dots . . .

The clearest example of this technique being consciously adopted comes from the 19th century Russian, Chekhov (another founder of the form) in his story 'The Bet'. In the first published version of the story, Chekhov tells how a wealthy businessman and a young lawyer have a reckless bet of two million roubles over whether the lawyer can voluntarily remain in solitary confinement for fifteen years. The lawyer moves into a lodge in the banker's garden and reads all the books the banker supplies him with, covering all the fields of human knowledge, methodically at first, then increasingly indiscriminately. On the eve of the completion of the fifteen years, the banker, now virtually bankrupt, goes to the cell to kill his 'prisoner'. He finds him asleep and haggard looking, with a note on the table. The note reveals that during his fifteen terrible years alone and meditating he has come to despise the banker and his millions, and to prove it will leave his cell five hours before the allotted time. The banker, filled with amazement and self-contempt, returns to his room. The lawyer indeed escapes. Several years later, however, a party at the banker's house is interrupted when the lawyer bursts in, desperate for money. The banker, overcome by the shock of his return and his demand, shoots him dead.

The tale as it stands has 'a beginning, a middle and an end.' Events have reached a bloody but satisfactory resolution by the time we finish, on a full stop. But when Chekhov included it in his *Collected Works*, he cut the final part and ended the story with the escape of the prisoner. This (the version now found in anthologies) leaves us pondering the reasons behind the lawyer's act, and the possible spiritual, psychological consequences for the banker. Chekhov was surely right in making this alteration. The power of the story is increased by the unnerving sensation of the implications being far from exhausted, of the ripples continuing to spread from its centre.

And Chekhov in fact said 'I think when one has finished writing a short story one should delete the beginning and the end', a method which led John Galsworthy to remark of Chekhov's stories that they were 'all middle, like a tortoise.' As such, they are significant scenes in a process which has begun before the story opens, and is understood to continue after the story has ended. This is very different from 'teaching a lesson about life', a function which any writer assumes at his peril. If a reader is keen to learn any lessons about life from literature then the moralist novel writers of the nineteenth century might be more suitable. It is in fact a feature of the short story that it often cannot be described as 'moral'. Its concern is more frequently with atmosphere, or mystery, or a brief evocation of the dynamics of a relationship. It creates a temporary world, explores an idea, and then withdraws. It can make a point, rather than teach a lesson. It is less well suited to the writer with a message to preach, than it is to the writer who has what Keats calls 'negative capability', that is, 'when a man is capable of being in uncertainties, mysteries, doubts, without any irritable reaching after fact or reason.' It is not surprising that many great short stories do not teach a lesson so much as depict an enigma, as we shall see later in the chapter.

Twist my tail, 4C!!

There is another feature often associated with the short story which has become valued out of all proportion, and that is the surprise ending. I once had the painful experience of having a seasoned English teacher interrupt my lesson to decree that 'a good short story has a twist at the end! 'The Monkey's Paw', Mr Birkett! Twist my tail, 4C, twist my tail!' She left me with the class, who were looking mildly anxious as they became aware yet again of their own experience being contradicted by the authoritative voice of a teacher. *Must* all stories have a twist at the end? Of course some do, the most famous being those of the American O. Henry. With great skill and ingenuity he repeatedly leads the reader to expect something other than what he gets, through such characters as Jeff Peters his brilliant confidence trickster. But used without enormous skill, such a

95

device can be a feeble trick, propping up a weak story or serving
only to invalidate, rather than add to, what has gone before, like
the sad refuge of so many children writers, 'And then I woke up
and it had all been a dream.'

If it works well, and it's extremely hard to do, then not only is
the sensation of our expectations being upset enormously
pleasurable, but we are then forced to see the preceding events
of the story in a new way. In Henry James' classic tale 'The
Turn of the Screw', a governess in a country house describes
the terrifying happenings there (she sees ghastly faces at the
window, and figures in the grounds) which convince her that the
spirits of two dead servants are attempting to gain possession of
the two delightful little children of the house. We become
hugely involved in her struggle to protect them, until in the final
pages she confronts them with these apparitions in an attempt to
'exorcise' them — but the children claim to see nothing, and are
so terrified, perhaps as a result of her tactics, that one is killed by
the shock and the other falls into a fever. The ending is
ambiguous: is it the governess who has been manipulated by the
powers of evil rather than the children? The reader is left in a
whirl reconsidering the complex chain of events in a new but
still uncertain way. The mystery of differing personal
interpretations of reality was something that fascinated James in
much of his writing, and while 'The Turn of the Screw' is, yes, a
'horror' story, and a 'story with a twist at the end', it is also about
people and the realities of living. The 'twist' is a part of that
reality, that uncertainty, rather than something used merely for
effect — though the effect is stunning.

'The grim phantasm, FEAR'

We can continue our analysis of the kinds of things short stories
are built around, and at the same time have a further look at the
story that attempts to unsettle the reader. It should be obvious
why the short story is so well suited to dealing with the
unknown. A good story of this kind relies less on the gruesome
or the macabre than on suspense or uncertainty, and these are
more easily sustained for a short time than over the hills and
valleys of a novel. What frightens us is as much psychological as
external: and if the main character is uncertain about what is
really happening, whether it's behind the locked door or within

his own mind, then the chances are the reader will be engrossed in fearful curiosity too. The 'Gothic' stories of Edgar Allan Poe are frequently built round the nervous, excitable sensibilities of their main characters, who infect the world of the story with their personalities, super-receptive to perceptions and imaginings of evil. Most of his characters are mildly deranged in some way, reclusive aristocrats, moody scholars of arcane lore — the ones played by Vincent Price in the Hollywood versions of *The Masque of the Red Death*, *Ligeia* and so on. One such is Roderick Usher, acutely aware that his mind is unbalanced, and that this makes him a prey to horrible imaginings:

> I dread the events of the future not in themselves, but in their results . . . I have, indeed, no abhorrence of danger, except in its absolute effect — in terror. In this unnerved — in this pitiable condition — I feel that the period will sooner or later arrive when I must abandon life and reason together, in some struggle with the grim phantasm, FEAR.

The trouble with this is that it's rather overdone, rather too 'Gothic'. With somebody so obviously nutty we tend to remain detached from what is happening inside his head. The same principle works better in a story previously quoted, Poe's 'The Tell-Tale Heart' (see p.72) where the narrator meticulously murders an old man, by whose eye he has become insanely fixated, and buries him under the floorboards. The police come, and the narrator becomes horrifiedly aware of the beating of the old man's heart beneath the floor. The sound grows until it threatens to deafen him, and he hysterically confesses to the deed, driven to wretched distraction by the way the detectives mockingly ignore the din in the room. The detectives, it becomes clear, have heard nothing. This almost comes as a surprise, so far have we entered into the murderer's mind.

Perhaps the best example of a sensation of fear being created psychologically rather than by spooky events is in Ambrose Bierce's story 'A Tough Tussle'. A confederate soldier is alone on guard in a moonlit forest. He knows that his enemies are somewhere in the vicinity preparing for an attack. He makes out in the shadows the shape of a dead Yankee soldier under the trees. He is tired and edgy, the light is uncertain. As the night draws on, he wonders if the Yankee is really dead . . . or hasn't he just moved a fraction? All his rational education tells him that dead men don't move. But the night is a long one. His defences crumble, and he panics. He ends up slashing frantically at the corpse, and in despair as he realises the madness of his action he kills himself. When the two mutilated bodies are found the next morning, the reaction of his commanding officer as he shakes his head at the carnage is that it must have been 'a tough tussle.'

The strength of this story is that it can't be shrugged off, can't be dismissed as referring to things which 'don't exist'. When we read a story about 'The Thing in the Loft', it isn't hard for us to reassure ourselves that, well, there aren't any Things in *our* loft. With Ambrose Bierce's story, no such easy way out is allowed. It may be true that we are unlikely to find ourselves on solitary watch over a body in a moonlit forest. Nonetheless, we have all experienced times when all our reason and knowledge have begun to crumble under the test of fear. What continues to disturb about Bierce's story is not only the macabre quality of the act itself, but the uneasy feeling of the flimsiness of rational defences.

Finally, as an example of a story which could not be categorised as a horror story but which is certainly powerful and unsettling, Hemingway's 'The Killers'. The plot is a model of simplicity. Two men come into an empty lunch bar somewhere in America. It emerges they are waiting for a man, a 'big Swede', to come in so that they can kill him. They wait but he does not come. They leave. Nick, a boy serving in the lunch bar, goes to find the Swede and tells him. The man shrugs it off, hopelessly. He remains lying on the bed with his face to the wall. The boy returns to the lunch bar: 'I can't stand to think about him waiting in the room and knowing he's going to get it. It's too damned awful.' 'Well', says the barman, 'you better not think about it.' But the fact is the boy *is* going to think about it, and so is the reader, and about the boy's fear.

Snapshots

For a short story to reverberate in the memory, it does not have to contain a dramatic or violent incident as these do. As haiku is to poetry, so the short story can be to fiction; a snapshot, a scene or two which suggests preceding and subsequent scenes. Whether it's in the creation of a particular atmosphere for instance, or giving us significant scenes in a relationship, the feeling can be created that we have merely had a glimpse of something that has already been, and will continue to be, in existence. Obviously the world of personal relationships is ideally suited to such an approach. The story 'Funeral' (examined in chapter 7) exploits this well. Hemingway's 'Hills Like White Elephants' (page 36) deals with a couple's half hour wait for a train connection on a deserted Spanish station. Their conversation, which gets nowhere and is 'about' nothing very much, forms the bulk of the story. She remarks that the hills look like white elephants, and is irritated by his lack of response. She says things are no fun any more, he says they will be after her 'awfully simple' operation. In the end, she assures him she 'feels fine.' End of story. By this time we have been made acutely aware of the despair and frustration and self-deception in the relationship, and continue to brood over it, so powerful is the atmosphere of the story created by the sterile conversation and the lethargy of the dusty station.

Another writer who gives us perfect photographs of a relationship is Katherine Mansfield. Her stories concern missed opportunities, tiny but disastrous misunderstandings between people, the touching impossible dreams of lonely individuals. This is taken from 'A Dill Pickle':

And then, after six years, she saw him again. He was seated at one of those little bamboo tables decorated with a Japanese vase of paper daffodils. There was a tall plate of fruit in front of him, and very carefully, in a way she recognized immediately as his 'special' way, he was peeling an orange.

He must have felt that shock of recognition in her for he looked up and met her eyes. Incredible! He didn't know her! She smiled; he frowned. She came towards him. He closed his eyes an instant, but opening them his face lit up as though he had struck a match in a dark room. He laid down the orange and pushed back his chair, and she took her little warm hand out of her muff and gave it to him.

'Vera!' he exclaimed. 'How strange. Really, for a moment I didn't know you. Won't you sit down? You've had lunch? Won't you have some coffee?'

She hesitated, but of course she meant to.

'Yes I'd like some coffee.' And she sat down opposite him.

'You've changed. You've changed very much,' he said staring at her with that eager, lighted look. 'You look so well. I've never seen you look so well before.'

'Really?' She raised her veil and unbuttoned her high fur collar. 'I don't feel very well. I can't bear this weather, you know.'

'Ah, no. You hate the cold . . .'

'Loathe it.' She shuddered. 'And the worst of it is that the older one grows . . .'

He interrupted her. 'Excuse me,' and tapped on the table for the waitress. 'Please bring some coffee and cream.' To her: 'You are sure you won't eat anything? Some fruit, perhaps. The fruit here is very good.'

'No, thanks. Nothing.'

'Then that's settled.' And smiling just a hint too broadly he took up the orange again. 'You were saying — the older one grows —'

As the story develops, we become aware that his careful solicitude for her, his nostalgic but carefully selected memories of their relationship, are simply aspects of his selfishness, his desire to have things just so, and that this selfishness is even more entrenched in him than when they were lovers. He is not a swine, she is not shattered by the meeting. We are just made to see with marvellous delicacy the ways they both handle the meeting — he nostalgic and therefore detached, she still in some ways caught up in the relationship. She slips off in the middle of one of his speeches when he is being dismissive about the past.

She had gone. He sat there, thunder-struck, astounded beyond words . . . And then he asked the waitress for his bill.

'But the cream has not been touched,' he said. 'Please do not charge me for it.'

The story is not only about the meeting but about their whole past relationship, and how they have come to view it.

The 'what if?' story

There are of course an infinite number of possible short stories, and little is to be gained from devising endless categories for them. But there is another kind of story which we have not yet looked at which we might learn something from. It is a form which has come to prominence in our own times and in some forms could even be termed 'experimental.' It is the kind of story which is based upon a single idea, frequently a fantastic one, and which simply develops that idea in a literary way. It is less concerned with a realistic portrayal of a situation than with saying 'What if . . .' and then taking it from there.

In H.G. Wells' story 'The Country of the Blind', a wanderer gets lost somewhere in the Andes and crosses into a completely unknown land where all the inhabitants are blind. Initially he is pleased with his apparent superiority; but as the story progresses he comes to feel more and more like a freak, an outsider. He is on the brink of succumbing to suggestions of having an operation on his eyes when he breaks away and escapes, over the mountains. The story is a powerful study of the pressures of conformity.

A more aesthetic, purely fantasy approach is taken by Jorge Luis Borges, whose stories spring from ideas such as an infinite library in which all the possible books in the world are stored, (including billions of volumes of meaninglessly scrambled letters, or books which differ only in a single letter from their neighbour), whose librarians have trudged its stairways for centuries trying to find the supposed book which will provide the key to the library's system. In 'The Circular Ruins' a man trains himself to dream over a long period of time, until he creates a dream child over whom he has control. 'In the dreamer's dream, the dreamed one awoke.' The dreamer loves and fears for the boy. One day the dreamer sees a fire raging:

> For a moment, he thought of taking refuge in the river, but then he knew that death was coming to crown his old age and absolve him of his labours. He walked into the shreds of flame. But they did not bite into his flesh, they caressed him and engulfed him without heat or combustion. With relief, with humiliation, with terror, he understood that he too was a mere appearance, dreamt by another.

Unsurprisingly, science fiction writers rely heavily on the one-idea, what-if story. One of the best is Ray Bradbury, if only because his stories do not rely on the props and paraphernalia of sci-fi, the gadgets and time-warps and androids and the rest of it. He gets hold of a good idea, works it out on the page, and is a good enough word-magician to sweep us along with him. His short story 'The Traveler' is built round the idea that his main character, a witch-girl called Cecy, can 'inhabit' anything and anyone she chooses. The story is really a vehicle for him to explore what this would feel like. And because it's beautifully and imaginatively written, it's very entertaining to read.

The clear incident, ended with a full stop; the straggle of dots that leaves the reader thinking; the twist in the tail; the story that unsettles; the snapshot story; the 'what-if' story . . . there are plenty more kinds, but we would need an encyclopaedia to cover them all. Many stories spread over several categories, as is always the way with writing and categories. I have tried to avoid the stock notions of the horror story, the love story, the crime story and so on, looking instead at what has provided the basis for some good short stories, the idea or situation from which they start and the way in which that is treated, in the hope that some knowledge of the variety of forms a short story can take will have been gained. Some of them may have given you the germs of ideas for stories of your own. Once you know the form a little you are better equipped to make it work for you.

IDEAS FOR WRITING

Look back into your own past. You will almost certainly have been involved in incidents which you have continued to brood over or tell other people about. Use one as the basis for a realistic short story.

Newspapers are full of small articles that briefly recount a dramatic or even sensational incident — a woman is found throwing £5 notes from a bridge; three people are found dead in a car having committed suicide in the belief that the end of the world was only hours away. (Both these are genuine). Collect a few, and build a short story around one of them, adding fictional characterisation, motivation and the events which led up to it.

Shakespeare regularly borrowed plots from minor, even trashy, writers of his day. It is still perfectly possible to find the germ of a good story in badly written magazine stories or anthologies — in fact seeing it done badly will help you towards seeing how it might be done well.

Two people work together in a shop. Their relationship is one of mutual irritation, developing into hatred. The silent warfare between them is conducted through the petty incidents and routines in the shop. One of them decides finally to crush or humiliate the other one with a carefully laid plan. The plan, however, backfires.

A funeral. As the mourners stand around the grave, the reader hears the thoughts of some of them. At the reception, the will is read out. The family and friends exchange a few brief comments. Over the course of the story an uncertainty about how the person died emerges. Alternatively, the manner of his death which seems unproblematic to the reader through the story suddenly appears to be other than that towards the end.

A girl works late in an office. She is perfectly relaxed, has plenty of work to do and plenty of time in which to do it. As the night draws on, she becomes increasingly aware of small noises in the empty building and of trivial, inexplicable events — objects not where she thought she had left them, and so on. Gradually her own certainty about her reactions begins to crumble, until she does not know if it is she herself or something in the building which is the cause of her fear. This leads her to a violent, irrational act.

A mother and son meet for their monthly lunch in a restaurant chosen by the mother. For both of them this is a ritual which they would not or could not forego, though for different reasons. In the snapshot of this regularly occurring appointment, try to suggest the forces at work in this relationship.

You are accidentally granted some magical power — to know what people are going to say just before they say it, to remember exactly everything that happened one year ago, to be in two places at once. This gift, or curse, only lasts twenty-four hours. Build a short story around one of those powers or a similar idea.

103

A reading list of short story writers

If you want to read, as well as write some short stories, this is a brief reading list. Such a list cannot fail to be anything but personal and incomplete and is specifically designed to accompany this chapter. If it were much longer it would be unmanageable, so many accomplished short story writers do not appear.

Of the writers who tend to end their stories with a full stop, are: Somerset Maugham, who frequently uses exotic settings for dramatic and finely crafted stories; Stan Barstow, Bill Naughton and Alan Sillitoe, who write stories with a clear story line and strong characterisation, often against a Northern working class background; and Frank O'Connor, whose sad and comic stories about Ireland and childhood are a treat.

The twist in the tail is the speciality of the American O. Henry, but also of the English writer Saki, who has a fine eye for irony and elegant grimness, particularly in the world of children.

Of the writers of stories which unsettle, my favourites are Edgar Allan Poe, Nathaniel Hawthorne and Ambrose Bierce, all nineteenth century(ish) Americans. They seem to unsettle you deeply, rather than nauseate you with gruesome detail or bore you with spooks.

Ian McEwan produces strong reactions of admiration or of loathing from many people, with his stories about sex and adolescence. I'm one of the admirers. Roald Dahl I find less unsettling than irritating, with his complicated stories of people being nasty to each other.

The best writers of the modern variety of short story, looser on narrative but tight on suggestion and implication, are in my opinion: Hemingway (very prolific — recommended are 'The Killers', 'Indian Camp', 'A Clean Well-lighted Place', 'Soldier's Home', 'The Short Happy Life of Francis Macomber', 'A Day's Wait'); Katherine Mansfield, who specialises in delicate analyses of people and relationships; D.H. Lawrence, whose stories are boldly written, varied tales of men and women, nature, sexuality; James Joyce, whose single collection *Dubliners* can be read again and again, so subtle, even enigmatic, are the stories in it; the stories of Albert Camus, who also wrote only one volume, *Exile and the Kingdom*, are philosophical in nature but written in a beautifully clear and simple style.

Finally, of the short story writers who write non-realistic fiction, Jorge Luis Borges stands in a class of his own with his exquisitely written tales of intellectual fantasy. Mention is also made in the chapter of Ray Bradbury, who can turn his hand to most things, including straight sci-fi.

10 What is a poem?

That may seem a silly question. Thousands of people today show they know the answer simply by writing poetry, even if they couldn't give, or wouldn't be interested in giving, a theoretical answer. I once heard an English poet describe how he took on the job of editing an anthology of contemporary unpublished poetry, for which he invited entries from anyone who wished to contribute no more than two poems. For the next few months he made daily trips to the local post office to collect numerous large red boxes into which the postmen had placed the day's flood of mail for him. Writing poetry comes naturally to many people, and is indeed synonymous for them with 'creative writing'. Nonetheless, there are perhaps an equally large number of potential writers who shy away from it, regarding poetry with anything from misty-eyed awe to butch contempt. To some it is the 'spontaneous overflow of powerful feeling'* or 'pure', undisciplined emotion, to others it is an impossibly complicated intellectual pursuit, to others it is soppy, to others mystical. (Poetry of course can be all these things, though it won't all necessarily be good poetry). Young children often pick up that it means freedom, experimentation, intensity, and write poetry with far more spontaneity and enthusiasm than their seniors, who begin to get suspicious of unfashionable emotions, or put off by old-fashioned language, or paralysed by their compulsorily developed awareness of rhyme schemes, assonance, dissonance, metres and all the rest of it.

There is no shortage of *definitions* of poetry, particularly from poets themselves. Matthew Arnold said 'Poetry is nothing less than the most perfect speech of man, that in which he comes nearest to being able to utter the truth.' The Romantic poet Coleridge said 'Poetry = the best words in the best order.' Boris Pasternak, rather more entertainingly, 'It is the crunch of jostling ice floes, it is two nightingales duelling'. It is nice to know that poets consider themselves to be engaged upon the

*Wordsworth's definition.

noblest of human activity, but it is not much help to us. How are
the nightingales made to duel? What are the best words? Why
can't this be done in prose, which seems so much more natural
to us? I was once asked by a student in a creative writing group
to define the differences between poetry and prose. Having
promised an answer in a few days, I thought about the jostling
ice floes, the best words and so on. Finally she got her answer:
'Poetry, unlike prose, is divided up into lines and arranged on a
page.' This seemed to me to sum it up pretty well, but she was
horrified. She pointed out that prose could then be turned into
poetry merely by arranging the words into lines on a page. This
was true, as long as she realised that it wouldn't, again,
necessarily be good poetry.

For instance:

'The Slopes of Mount Terror'

We have heard of Cape Crozier
(The eastern extremity of Ross Island)
Discovered by Ross, and named
After the captain of the Terror.
It is here
With immense pressures and rending
The moving sheet of the Barrier
Piles itself against the mountain.

It is here, also, that the ice cliff
Which runs for hundreds of miles to the east,
With the barrier behind it, and the Ross sea
Beating into its crevasses and caves
Joins the Basalt precipice which bounds the Knoll . . .

It is the kind of place
Where giants have had a good time in their childhood
Playing with ice instead of mud.

> from *The Worst Journey in the World* by Apsley
> Cherry-Garrard.

These lines, with only one or two minor alterations, come
from a journal of Antarctic exploration, and the result is not a
marvellous, but not an awful, poem. The arrangement of the

lines makes us read it in a particular way, bringing out certain
rhythms and emphasising particular phrases which help to bring
out the grandeur and power of the scenery. It seems that only
travel books will allow that kind of poetry to be 'found' ready
made in their pages. But here's some social comment:

'Philip looks in on Soho's Big Clean-up'

Prince Philip

Gave the royal seal of approval
To the West End's clean-up campaign today
When he went walkabout
In the streets of Soho

The Prince
Exchanged the state carriage
Of the Queen Mother's birthday celebrations
For a fifteen-minute stroll
Through the gaudy streets that used to be congested with litter.
There was a happy surprise
For many Soho shopkeepers
As the Prince passed their stores.

For a crowded and often
Unrespectable area there was a complete lack
Of ugly incidents.

In Leicester Square
One of the resident tramps
Was prevented from making a rush
To button-hole the Prince
By security men.

This is taken entirely, including the title, from the
*Evening Standard.**

Just the fact that it's been made into a poem, with a 'little
incident' given the important place at the end, makes us
approach it in a different way, and in this case detect a sarcasm
that we can be sure wasn't there in the original.

This technique, of 'discovering' poems in unlikely pieces of
prose, is called 'Found Poetry' and it's good fun to do. Quite

*Thursday, 17th July, 1980.

logically, it can be done the other way round too, turning poems into respectable pieces of prose. If the poem has a regular rhythm and easily noticeable rhyme ('This is the Night Mail crossing the border/Bringing the cheque and the postal order') then the prose version of it will sound completely unnatural. A piece of modern free verse, however, could be written as prose, as in this 'version' of Richard Aldington's 'Evening':

'The chimneys, rank on rank, cut the clear sky; the moon, with a rag of gauze about her loins, poses among them, an awkward Venus. And here am I, looking wantonly at her over the sink.'

Quite simply, however, it does better what it wants to do as a poem.

> The chimneys, rank on rank,
> Cut the clear sky;
> The moon,
> With a rag of gauze about her loins
> Poses among them, an awkward Venus —
> And here am I looking wantonly at her
> Over the sink.

The spacing just makes it easier to read, slows us down in the right way for the mood of the poem, particularly, making us pause before the last two lines, and separates out the 'ideas' for us. It gives them, however simply, a kind of *form*. That's a word we'll have to come back to in another chapter.

The poet and literary critic William Empson quotes a fragment of a Chinese translation:

> Swiftly the years, beyond recall
> Solemn the stillness of this spring morning.

The two statements confront us, the making of some significant relationship is up to us. We connect, probably, movement in the first line and stillness in the second (though of course we may not do so consciously). Similarly, the years of the first line, and the moment in the second, and so on. This only points to the fact that the *reader* is likely to know what poetry 'is', will know its unwritten 'conventions', but that fact is important to the writer. It gives an indication of how the simplest, most basic use of poetic form, that of writing two lines separately in sequence, affects the way we look at a piece of writing.

The conventions of poetry have changed over thousands of years. Before men could write, and this is still true in many non-literate societies, poems were committed to memory with some sections improvised, by professional bards and recited at important occasions. Unsurprisingly they had strong regular rhythms and repeated phrases, an aid to memory among other things. With the development of writing, the 'pattern' of poetry came to include the eye as well as the ear. The simplest nursery rhyme shares a common origin with a sonnet of Keats or Eliot's *Four Quartets*. But do they have anything in common *now*, which, to go back to our student's question, make them different from prose? We have arrived at an exasperatingly simple distinction that poetry is spaced in lines on a page, but we should now ask, to what end?

Neither a rabbit, nor a bolt of lightning

If there is any one idea which links almost every writer of almost every kind of poem, it is the idea that somehow poetry involves magic — not in its creation, but in its effect. I mean magic here in a sense squarely between the magic of the professional conjuror and the magic of the 'primitive'. Between, that is, what is completely explicable and what is completely inexplicable. The conjuror's audience knows that somewhere he is concealing a struggling rabbit before he materialises it with a flourish (though unless he's an idiot he won't reveal where). The primitive does not understand why certain thiings happen (lightning, let us say), and ascribes them to a magical force which is not given to him, and will never be given to him, to understand. A poem is neither a rabbit produced from a top hat, nor a divine bolt of lightning, though it has something in common with both. The poet uses everything at his disposal to create his own kind of magic. If there is no sense at all of the marvellous when we read a poem, then it is perhaps a bad poem — unless of course it is we who are bad readers. The poet uses his knowledge of language, its associations, forms, rhythms and so on to create his magic. But he is hardly like the conjuror who knows perfectly well how his trick works. The poet will, every time, have to rely on instinct to help him juggle all the elements of his poem successfully. (Nobody can give you instinct, but you can train it and guide it. Perhaps that's why you're reading this book). After his poem is finished he may marvel almost as much as an enthusiastic reader, not (not always, anyway) because he is swollen with conceit, but because he really won't entirely understand the process in the way that the conjuror does. There is no point in looking at a poem, then, as if it were a series of tricks. But nor is it a total mystery. A good poem has something of both. Here it might be safe to quote a poet's definition which could be of some practical use to us. The American William Carlos Williams said simply 'A poem is a machine made out of words.' The point about a machine is that it has to be designed, worried over, and built; and when it is built, it appears, almost magically, to have a life of its own.

It's high time we had a look at a complete poem. Here is 'Terrace', by Sue Shrapnel, from *Hackney Writers' Workshop Vol.3*

'Terrace'

At the front, the houses try to part from each other,
fence fights with hedge,
paint rivals paint.
Net curtains defend: the defenceless are suspect.
Wallflowers compete.

At the back, dustbins and children and cats
and washing-lines open us out.
Smiles cross through kitchen windows,
hands cross walls with sugar and tools.
Children dream in the yard as their parents row in the house;
a man mutters to the onions, wagging a finger;
a woman stands short of breath with pegs in her hand.
At night, someone with a skinful
kicks a bottle;
at dawn, a brick scrapes
as a lover uncovers a key.
At the back there are no secrets, but we all keep them.

At the front, everything is hidden, and talk is merciless.

Word Power

If you like this, you may be led to wonder what makes it a good poem. Its main idea is really very simple, the contrast drawn is a straightforward one, the lives of the people concerned couldn't appear less unusual. The language isn't showy or elaborate. Yet personally I often find myself looking at terrace houses and thinking about that poem, and vice versa.

For one thing, it's a lovely relaxed view of backyard communities. Everything is clearly and perfectly observed:

> At the back, dustbins and children and cats . . .
> a woman stands short of breath with pegs in her hand

The details are right, and there's always a charm simply in that, in being taken so quickly and fully into the world of a poem. But as in a well-edited film, the details are helping suggest an idea:

> Smiles cross through kitchen windows
> hands cross walls with sugar and tools.

We're bound to respond to the image of hands crossing walls, particularly after we've been told how at the front, the houses try to part from each other. But it's only 'sugar and tools' that are being handed over, there's no need to be romantic about this down-to-earth communion. There *is* a feeling, though, a sense of marvel at the ordinary, of love even, for the familiar noises of the backyard, the bottle breaking, the brick grating. Then:

> At the back, there are no secrets, but we all keep them.
> At the front, everything is hidden, and talk is merciless.

Nowhere does the poem directly ask why, but the question, and an answer, is implicit in it. So we don't feel we are being preached at, but that an idea is being worked out in front of us. The idea isn't presented baldly to us at the beginning, it's stretching its limbs on the page. In that sense it's a performance — and here we might risk another definition, not anybody else's this time, that a poem is the performance of an idea. And you can't have one without the other.

I began with 'Terrace' because without being elaborate or complex, it does exemplify several things common to most good poems. A good use of images, first of all. An image is a word-picture, in this poem of a fairly straightforward kind: 'fence fights with hedge', 'Smiles cross through kitchen windows'. There's plenty to see and hear. It contains an idea, upon

which the poem is built, the contrast between back and front.
Her language is simple, but is used not only to sketch precise
images, but also to pinpoint paradox:

> Net curtains defend: The defenceless are suspect . . .
> At the back, there are no secrets, but we all keep them.

Finally there is feeling, intensity, seriousness, sincerity, whatever we choose to call it. She cares about what she is writing
without tipping her emotion all over us. So it's feeling with
control.

We can perhaps draw up a list of the four things which we
consider important in writing poetry:

A poetic idea, on which the poem is built, the angle from
which it approaches its subject matter.

Imagery, which roots the ideas and emotions of the poem in
the physical world.

A sensitive use of language, that is, the feel for the right word,
which can sometimes be the plainest one, at the right time.

Feeling with control: feeling needs to come through if we are
to respond to the poet-in-the-poem. (This is not to say that
he has to be sincere all the time and say only what *he* thinks.
He can play roles as much as he likes, so long as each one
convinces us.) Feeling won't by itself sustain a poem. It needs
to be drawn into the poem's whole.

The list is slightly absurd because any such list would be. No
good poem was ever written to a recipe, and plenty of good
poems could be found in which other things are more important.
But it will do as a working rule.

11 Just a few lines

Wisely forgetting our poetic list for a while, we could think about beginning to write some poetry straight away. But there are few things more frustrating than the generous invitation to write a poem about anything. So this will have self-imposed restrictions in the hope of providing a simple framework and discipline. The form I want to begin by looking at is a traditional Japanese one known as haiku. The rules are strict. The aim is to present an image, evoke a mood, or make an observation — in three lines. What's more, the number of syllables per line is also controlled: five in the first, seven in the second, five in the third. This 'perfect' haiku is by a girl of 12.

	syllables
Running through the snow	5
Cold and numb gallops the horse	7
Challenging the train	5
	total 17

This 'imperfect' haiku is by the American poet Ezra Pound.*

> 'In a station of the Metro'
>
> The apparition
> Of these faces in the crowd;
> Petals on a wet, black bough

It is 'imperfect' only in the sense that the last line contains seven rather than five syllables. But like the girl's above, it presents an image, or rather, two, which trigger off a kind of emotional response in us. In the girl's, it is perhaps a simple one of

---

*Pound wrote the poem in *two* lines: but otherwise it follows the haiku format.

admiration for the cold, numb horse, pitted against the train. In Pound's, the word 'apparition' gives the poem a dream-like quality, which is picked up again in the last line 'Petals on a wet, black bough' which suggests a special kind of sympathy with the anonymous faces on the platform.

Many haikus, including the two above, work in much the same way as a photograph, primarily on the visual level. And, like a photograph, they present an image in such a way and in such a relation to the other things in the poem (or photograph) that we 'read' the finished product as a whole. In this case, we see the faces in the metro and the petals together. Within the poem they are the same thing. Already we can see what can be done in three lines.

This is a famous haiku, also by Pound:

> 'Fan-Piece, for her Imperial Lord'
>
> O fan of white silk
> Clear as frost on the grass blade
> You also are laid aside

We are probably struck by the beauty of the central image, but immediately we have to read it again. Whatever the poem is 'about', we can see, almost touch, the fan itself. The title helps us, but the word 'also' is interesting, too. It suggests a whole range of experience similar to, but outside, the one in the poem. It's happened before. The speaker, we guess, is a figure in some kind of court intrigue, whose identity isn't certain. There's plenty for the reader to 'do' here.

There's plenty for the writer to do with haikus, too. The aim is perfection of a sort, and that's always worth striving for. Any experience will do for your material — a view from a train, an action caught in snapshot, a mood, a comparison. But keep to the rules as a form of discipline, and keep revising and rejecting until you have the essence of what you want to do. Of course you may not know exactly what you want to do until you see it on the page in front of you. That's half the fun. The haikus that follow are by some of my students.

'Bank Holiday Heatwave'

Between the quick scoop
And the greedy lick, a sadness:
Warm vanilla on the knuckle

'Moments later'

Fingers sweat-cool, eyes
defreeze their ardour; already
sunlight trails on cold water

'Loneliness'

Thoughts clawing the night
for touch-familiar-warmth; but
only a firebreak in the east

'Hysteria'

Bewildering splits
and tricky little metal zips
revealing the unconscious

'Old pair of sandals'

My foot's curled imprint
Sleeps in the patient leather
Ready for my careless dash

Without the trappings

We can now go on to think of other ways of writing satisfying
poems which don't take six weeks, and if we're lucky not even
six minutes. One of the good things about a haiku is that it's so
short there's no room for vagueness or waffle. It's got to be clear
and sharp. 'Vagueness' is in fact something that has always been
a problem with the writing of poetry. Poems can often look
'poetic' if they wrap themselves up in an artificial, or sentimental, or old-fashioned kind of language: but give them a push

116

and the icing falls off to leave nothing very interesting underneath. Around the time of the First World War, a group of poets calling themselves 'Imagists' began to reject the kind of poetry which reflected and glorified the self of the writer, or which relied on elaborate poetic language to disguise the essential banality of the thoughts. They wanted poems to be 'hard', impersonal, relying heavily on precisely constructed images. Ezra Pound was one of the foremost Imagist poets, and said, interestingly, 'Poetry must be as well written as prose' — by which he meant that it was no use dressing up stale ideas and sentiments in the outward forms of poetry if they would be exposed for what they were in plain prose. Richard Aldington's poem 'Evening', quoted in the previous chapter, is an 'Imagist' poem, and we've seen that it stands up pretty well to Pound's test. It isn't being propped up by anything.

This is one of their 'poems without the trappings':

'The Encounter'

All the while they were talking the new morality
Her eyes explored me.
And when I arose to go
Her fingers were like the tissue
Of a Japanese paper napkin

Ezra Pound

Even in these five lines we do in fact find our four elements: *imagery* and a *sensitive use of language* — the paper napkin image at the end most strikingly, but there's also a note of contempt in the phrase 'talking the new morality'; *poetic idea,* the idea upon which the poem is based, here the gap between the hot air being talked and the action going on silently; and *feeling with control,* in the ironic tone of voice used to make the point.

Of course we might complain that we've never actually *felt* a Japanese paper napkin, and that this delicate observation-making is a bit 'precious'. Doesn't the combination, though, of 'tissue', 'Japanese' and 'paper' *suggest* an extreme sensual lightness, even if we've never been near the thing itself? Some people at the time were quick to notice the dangers of this style, and a parody was written which poked fun at just this:

> 'Selected Bulbs from a Javan Pot'
>
> Wondering how I would be able to pay my
> laundress, I let my eyes fall and I saw the
> smutty tamarinds I grow in my little window-box

The idle life of the literary dabbler is mocked in the mention of the laundress and the exotic flowers, but there's more to it than that. The writer of the parody has pushed the three line poem over from lightness to triviality. It doesn't work as a *poem* (deliberately) because the two images (laundress' bills, smutty tamarinds) don't 'charge' each other. There is nothing dynamic in the gap between them, they are not in any interesting relationship to each other. Unlike Pound's 'Encounter' where the talk and the touch are in a relationship of ironic contrast. Or the haiku 'Moments Later'; where the bodily images (fingers, sweat, eyes) 'charge' the natural ones (sunlight, cold water) and vice versa.

Here's another example of an 'Imagist' poem:

> 'Oread'
>
> Whirl up, sea —
> Whirl your pointed pines
> On our rocks
> Hurl your green over us,
> Cover us with your pools of fir
>
> by H.D.

This will also help to introduce what is in many ways the staple of poetry: metaphor. Metaphor, any schoolteacher will tell you, is a way of comparing one thing with another without using 'like' or 'as'; and it's usually paired with simile, which is a comparison which *does* use 'like' or 'as'. But the comparison isn't always conscious in metaphor. There's nothing very sophisticated about metaphor, we use it all the time. Look at the following sentence: 'He came storming into the bar, a mountain of a man with a bull neck and cauliflower ears, shot a look at the barman and exploded with laughter.' A bit startling as a sentence, but each phrase is a perfectly ordinary expression. Each phrase is also metaphorical. The man is compared to a storm, a mountain, a bull, a cauliflower, a gun, a piece of dynamite — except that we don't really notice the comparison because the phrases are so common. We *do* notice it in metaphors in good poetry because they are fresh and original.

The poem above, 'Oread', is based on one metaphor, that of 'the-sea-as-pines'. There have been a million poems about the sea but this is new because the metaphor is new. Just as you can hardly speak without using some kind of metaphor, so a poet comes to write in metaphor almost as second nature:

> The day *dispossessed* of light. At four o'clock
> in the afternoon, a sulphurous, *manufactured*
> twilight, *smudging* the scummed lake's far side
> *leant* on the park

> from 'October in Clowes Park' by Tony Connor (with my italics)

A poem, then, particularly of the kind we are considering, can be built around a single metaphor*. The same is true of a simile. These next three, by students, are of the second kind.

'Marauder'

Invading my heart,
Like a cloud of jet-black ink
From a squid, is love

'Resurgence'

You jump in and out of my life
Like some bad-mannered
Out of time Jack-in-the-box.
Just when I have changed
Just when I need you least,
You come jumping back
With only a slight limp

*See also Chapter 12, 'Ideas into Shape'.

'The Sip'

Like wine
I feel him in me
Warming the world
With his colour

This one, translated from a classical Indian language, uses two similes to make a relationship of contrast:

'What she said'

When my lover is by my side
I am happy
as a city
in the rapture of a carnival,

and when he is gone
I grieve like a deserted house
of the wastelands
where the squirrel plays
in the front yard

Seeing double

In all creative writing, relationships between things (words, images, situations, events) are of overriding interest. We have seen relationships at work in the two-line fragment:

Swiftly the years, beyond recall
Solemn the stillness of this spring morning

They are there in Pound's 'Encounter', and absent in the parody, 'Selected Bulbs'. One of the most interesting relationships in writing is that of irony. It's not an easy word to define, but we recognise it when we see it, and in fact use it ourselves all the time. When a person sourly says 'Charming!', we know by their face that they mean quite the opposite, and we respond to the relationship between what they say and how they say it. That familiar kind of relationship is not, perhaps, incredibly fascinating (what I've just written is another kind of irony, that of understatement). We see this too in the comic-book slang as the flak-shredded fighter pilot staggers into the

mess and says quietly, 'Spot of bother over the Channel ...
Jerry wanted a dust-up so I obliged ... suppose I'll need a bit of
sewing-up.' Again the effect is in a relationship, between the
nature of the situation and what's said about it.

When someone speaks to us, we can see the expression on
their face and react accordingly. When someone speaks in a
deliberately deadpan way, we have to guess a little at how they
want their words to be taken. And when a writer writes
ironically, we are made to work a little harder than that. As soon
as we grasp the writer's intentions, we feel we know something
not immediately obvious in the statement.

'By Omission'

Time
For my black brother
Began with his slavery
Or so my history master said.

Les Skeates (*Hackney Writers' Workshop*)

We are immediately drawn into a conspiracy with the writer
against the history master who makes this statement — the
'interesting relationship' being between the facts of black history
and the assumptions behind the schoolmaster's remark. We are
seeing double, through the eyes of the writer and of the speaker.

Talk about irony always runs the risk of being obvious
because irony is such a common part of our speech. The
schoolboy who wrote this poem didn't need to be told what irony
was:

'Broadminded'

Some of my best friends are white boys.
When I meet 'em
I treat 'em
Almost as if they was people

Ray Durem

121

Nor do we as readers need to have it explained. Nonetheless, it isn't always easy to see how it works. Yet the process is essentially the same for this poem as it is for what is perhaps English Literature's most famous ironic sentence: 'It is a truth universally acknowledged that a single man in possession of a good fortune must be in want of a wife.' Universally acknowledged by whom, we wonder . . . and enter into a conspiracy with Jane Austen as she satirizes the matchmaking mothers of the English upper classes. It is a conspiracy because it is a way of mocking someone without them knowing about it. The history master's statement, too, appears to be given absolutely 'straight'.

Irony clearly can't be confined either to poetry or to prose. But it should also be obvious that the ironic tone of voice is extremely well suited to the poem of a few lines, as we have seen above, and also in the student's poem below. In all three examples, thought processes are started and left for the reader to finish.

> 'Revelation'
>
> Exhibitionist
> I am:
> baring my soul
> to anyone
> who will tell me
> it is still there.

Again, we are left thinking about the two apparently contradictory statements, and the relationship between them. D.H. Lawrence, too, was fond of the ironic, and here also very bitter, tone:

> 'The mosquito knows'
>
> The mosquito knows full well, small as he is
> he's a beast of prey.
> But after all
> he only takes his bellyful,
> he doesn't put my blood in the bank.

One thing to notice about many of these poems is how much can be done with a title. 'Fan-Piece, for her Imperial Lord' puts the feelings of the poem into an elaborate context. 'Moments Later' immediately presupposes an event, the nature of which we must guess at from the poem itself. 'Broadminded' prepares us, quite deliberately, for something slightly different from what we get. A good title helps you create a context, or strike a tone of voice, which will lead the reader to expect something. It may not be quite what the reader expects, of course.

Writing poetry of this kind shouldn't be seen *only* as a stepping-stone to writing longer poems. Haiku, for example, is a form many Japanese poets spent years perfecting and polishing. The aim of such poems is generally to make a point, or an observation, and withdraw. As such they need a sense of economy and a lightness of touch. These are also, in fact, qualities which will prove valuable in attempting any longer work. In the writing of poems like these, you should be able to start developing a practical understanding of the relationship between images, the use of simile and metaphor, and the possibilities of irony, all of which are fundamental to any kind of creative writing. You should also have an early taste of what every writer, professional or amateur, needs: a finished product to show for your efforts.

IDEAS FOR WRITING

Keeping to the rules if you can, write one or more haikus on any topic, using this list of suggestions if you need to:
  Peeling an orange
  A passerby seen from your window
  The rain in the street
  A bird on the chimney
  A moment of anger
  Traffic jam
  An animal moving

Write a poem of a few lines which uses a simile or a metaphor to give it form (see pages 125-135). Short love poems, or poems which express an intense emotion, are well suited to this.

Leave a short note for someone in the form of a poem giving what looks like an apology for something you've done. This could benefit from being ironic.

Use the following 'pattern' to write a short poem:
What I like about . . . is its . . .
What I hate about . . . is their . . .
What I like about . . . is her . . .

Write a poem describing the images you see as you drift off to sleep, or daydream.

Again using only images, write a short poem describing any of these:
Bank holiday on the beach
Winter evening
Memories of childhood
Household noises
Motorway service station
Private fears

12 Ideas into shape

Arranging your ideas

If we are agreed that the major characteristic of poetry is that it is arranged in lines on a page, we might also try and find out what kind of 'arranging' can be done and what effects it has. This chapter looks briefly at some of the different kinds of 'shape' or 'form' or 'structure' or 'pattern' a poem can have. The fact that words like 'shape' and 'pattern' are being used should reassure the reader that what follows is not a detailed, complex list of the different rules which apply when writing heroic couplets or quatrains, or whatever.* The simple fact is that poetry writing these days is not governed by rigid rules in the way that it was in, say, the 17th and 18th centuries. It is, nevertheless, important to consider what kind of 'shape' a poem is going to have, and how this might help you do what you want to do. After all, a poem is the performance of an idea, not just the statement of it.

The 'arrangements' which give a poem shape can be of many different kinds. There could be a rhyme at the end of each line, or every other line:

> How fevered is the man who cannot look
> Upon his mortal days with temperate blood,
> Who vexes all the leaves of his life's book
> And robs his fair name of its maidenhood.

These lines in fact not only rhyme alternately, but have a clear rhythm to them — there are five clear beats in each line:

> How févered ís the mán who cánnot lóok
> Upón his mórtal dáys with témperate blóod

So in these lines of John Keats', we derive a sense of shape from both rhyme and rhythm.

* Those who are interested in the technicalities of poetry are recommended to try Robin Skelton's excellent book *Teach Yourself Poetry* which contains a fair amount of technical instruction.

Or, there are sometimes whole lines or parts of lines repeated at a particular point in each verse in a refrain or chorus, as in this extract from a poem by a 14 year old, Sarah Gillam:

> I gave the letter to the old man's wife.
> I knew the problems would lie ahead.
> 'John fought hard', or so they told;
> The rain fell hard, the mines, the dead.
>
> I saw her cry, the old man's wife,
> I dried her eyes, pulled back her head,
> 'John died fighting', or so they told:
> The rain fell hard, the mines, the dead.

This kind of pattern is borrowed from the old ballad form, which was often sung, and therefore needed a regular rhythm. The choruses provide a pleasing bit of familiarity in each verse, and can serve to drive home the important images, in this case, of death and horror.

A pattern may be evident in the way the ideas of the poem are presented, so that the reader feels the thoughts and the actions following a pattern, as in this type of question and answer poem:

> 'O what do you here so late?' said the knight on the road,
> 'I'm going to meet my God' said the child as he stood,
> 'O how will you go by land?' said the knight on the road,
> 'With a strong staff in my hand,' said the child as he stood.

and so on. The boy is being tested by the knight (the devil disguised) and his questions become more and more menacing. So while there is repeated pattern, it also allows for development.

Or a poem may follow a pattern laid down by established rules. A sonnet, for instance, *has* to have fourteen lines, and these fourteen lines are themselves governed by rules about rhythm, length, and development of ideas. (An example is given on page 131).

Or, finally, it may only be from the development of the ideas and emotions that a sense of shape or structure emerges, in the way, for example, that the poem leads finally towards some kind of resolution. George Herbert, in 'The Collar', spends most of the poem grumbling and fretting about the priest's life he has to lead, but the poem finishes:

> But as I raved and grew more fierce and wild
>   At every word,
> Methought I heard one crying 'Child',
>   And I replied, 'My Lord'.

This is not to say that *every* poem has to have a noticeable shape or form. What a clear form can help to do is give a poem 'personality' — a word borrowed from the poet Robin Skelton, who gives a marvellously precise definition of what form is. Established forms, he says, tend 'to limit the personality of the poem, and therefore to strengthen and define it'. Personality in poems is linked with their pattern, their shape, their feel. The pattern of a poem, made up of its rhythms, its rhymes, its repetitions, its paradoxes, the arrangements of its ideas and so on, will make it crude, or subtle, or enchanting, or low-key, or monotonous, or whatever. All these things, together with the imagery and the tone of voice used, help to turn lines on a page into a 'performance'.

The external features of a poem (like rhythm and rhyme or the rules which it is following) frequently work together with the internal ones (the way in which the ideas are presented) to create the structure of a poem, each one strengthening the other. This is in a sense only an extension of the idea outlined in Chapter 10 'What is a poem?', that two lines written one after the other are placed in some kind of relationship with each other.

For discussion purposes, the external and internal features of a poem will be looked at separately.

Rhyme and rhythm

The most obvious thing to say about rhyme is also the most important: don't let your need for a rhyme dictate what you want to say. You'll end up twisting the sense uncomfortably. (Rhyme used well has just the opposite effect: it gives a statement a feeling of ease and perfection.) Someone wanting to write a love poem, for instance, has to watch out they don't fall into the arms/charms, tears/fears, ruby lips/fingertips trap.

These days, rhyme is much less frequently used than it used to be. But it's worth noting that rhyme is very popular: two of Britain's best-selling poets, John Betjeman and Pam Ayres, rely on it heavily. Greetings cards are nearly always rhymed and presumably give satisfaction because they are so. It's our need for pattern again, which comes out very strongly in song. Song always has a musical pattern (that's after all what music is), and nearly always a verbal pattern. One effect of rhyme can be to give a satisfying sense of neatness, of finality:

> Sexual intercourse began
> In nineteen sixty three
> (Which was rather late for me)
> Between the time of the Chatterley ban
> And the Beatles' first LP
>
> from 'Annus Mirabilis'
> by Philip Larkin

Or in the hands of someone like W.B. Yeats, who never lost his hold on strong, well-formed verse, strongly rhymed and rhythmed, it contributes to the effect of magical spell, of unassailable wisdom:

> Many times man lives and dies
> Between his two eternities,
> That of race and that of soul,
> And ancient Ireland knew it all.
> Whether man die in his bed
> Or the rifle knocks him dead,
> A brief parting from those dear
> Is the worst man has to fear.

Poetic ideas

As suggested earlier, a poem's shape can come as much from inside as from outside, in the way that the ideas and emotions are presented. It can in fact come entirely from what is referred to in 'What is a poem?' as a 'poetic idea'. A 'poetic idea' might be defined as a 'slant', an 'angle', a 'device' around which a poem can be built. In 'Terrace' it was the contrast between what happens at the front and what happens at the back of people's houses. In the following (student's) poem, the angle, the ideas which gives the poem its shape, is the similarity and contrast between love in the world of advertisements and love in real life.

'Light up'

Our heads almost touching
Our hands the other's cupping
We strike a match
                          And light up,
The glowing orange warmth spreads
Radiates and sparkles from your face
And in the loveliness
                          I breathe.
Surely smoothness has never been so
                          satisfying.
But
Moments that happiness blends
Moments and moods
          That set the made for each other
                          trend
The Surgeon General advises
And statutorily Warns —
          As butts,
          Must soon be tossed away

The idea is taken further to make the comparison between smoking and love: the 'butts/must soon be tossed away.' What makes the poem go on surviving re-readings is the deftness with which he mixes the false sincerity of the advertising world, the ambivalence of the spark of tenderness and the lighting of a

cigarette, the nasty after-effects of both, and the play with the
stale clichés of advertising language:

> Moments and moods
> > That set the made for each other
> > > trend

The notion of a poetic idea is nothing particularly new. Love,
for example, has always been elaborately, sarcastically and
joyfully compared with other things, from the pair of compasses
in John Donne's seventeenth century poem, to the twentieth
century cigarette advertisement, quoted here. Just as poets have
always adapted ideas and the form with which to express them
from previous poems, so it would be useful to you to look out in
the poems you read for the governing idea which a poem is
structured around and how it is used. Time spent experimenting
with old forms is often time well spent.

Bob Dylan's great song 'A Hard Rain's A-gonna Fall', uses a
question-answer ballad form, most well-known in the traditional
'Lord Randal'. The poem begins:

> O Where have you been, Lord Randal my son?
> O Where have you been, my handsome young man?

and these lines are used at the beginning of each verse, to which
the son gives enigmatic and increasingly ominous replies.
Finally it emerges that his lover has poisoned him. Dylan's song
keeps the questions, slightly adapted, at the beginning of each
verse, to which the replies are all descriptive of a horrifying,
senseless world. It's a modern protest song:

> Oh, who did you meet, my blue-eyed son?
> Who did you meet, my darling young one?
> I met a young child beside a dead pony,
> I met a white man who walked a black dog,
> I met a young woman whose body was burning,
> I met a young girl, she gave me a rainbow,
> I met one man who was wounded in love,
> I met another man who was wounded with hatred,
> And it's a hard, it's a hard, it's a hard, it's a hard
> It's a hard rain's a-gonna fall.

The forms and the poetic ideas are there to be used, where appropriate. What matters is that the voice and the concerns are yours.

Putting the two together: sonnets

A sonnet has a very clear internal and external shape. There are rules about the number of lines, and about the rhyme and the rhythm, and there are also rules about how the ideas should be organised. The rules are:

a) the poem is fourteen lines long
b) the lines rhyme alternately with each other in pairs:

> When in disgrace with Fortune and men's eyes,
> I all alone beweep my outcast state,
> And trouble deaf heaven with my bootless* cries,
> And look upon myself and curse my fate,

except for the last two lines which rhyme with each other:

> For thy sweet love remembered such wealth brings,
> That then I scorn to change my state with kings.

c) There are ten syllables in each line, with a stress on every second syllable:

> When in disgrace with Fortune and men's eyes

If all that sounds rather complicated and unnecessary, the complete sonnet, by Shakespeare, might make things clearer:

> When in disgrace with Fortune and men's eyes,
> I all alone beweep my outcast state,
> And trouble deaf heaven with my bootless cries,
> And look upon myself and curse my fate.
> Wishing me like to one more rich in hope,
> Featured like him, like him with friends possessed,
> Desiring this man's art, and that man's scope,
> With what I most enjoy contented least.
> Yet in these thoughts myself almost despising,

*useless

Haply I think on thee, and then my state,
Like to the lark at break of day arising
From sullen earth sings hymns at heaven's gate,
  For thy sweet love remembered such wealth brings
  That then I scorn to change my state with kings.

In this sonnet the speaker complains of loneliness (in the first four lines) and envy (in the next four lines). Then his thoughts turn to his loved one (in the next four) and he finally realises how lucky he is (in the final two lines). In this kind of sonnet, then*, the ideas are arranged in a particular pattern which is made clearer by the rhyme and also by the rules which govern how the lines are arranged, the poem's structure. The first four lines go together, are 'held in' by the rhymes, as are the second four, and so on.

Here is a young writer putting those rules, and the principles behind them, into practice:

'The four men'

The man approached the place of the four men.
You come to take my sleep? said the sleeper,
I do not want your sleep, so sleep again.
You come to take my food? said the eater,
I do not want your food, I have enough.
Do you come for my thoughts? said the thinker,
I do not want your thoughts, your thoughts may bluff.
Do you come for my drink? said the drinker,
I have no thirst so drink all you can.
I am the joker and I come to fool,
I shall keep joking as when life began.
I'll take your heart and stuff it till it's full,
I'll take your brains and carve them with my knife,
And what I come for, I shall steal — your life.

                Darrol Kenworthy.

The author of this sonnet is eleven years old, but has an excellent instinctive grasp of what a poetic form is for. The lines

*There are other kinds too: this one is known as the 'English' sonnet form.

132

form a pattern which *reflect* the pattern of the thoughts. The poem falls into two halves: in the first the men are uncertain as to who the visitor is, in the second he tells them. Within the first half there is also the question-answer pattern, which builds up suspense; and the most deadly words of the poem, 'your life', come neatly where they should, at the end, rhyming firmly with the line above to give a 'no argument' feel to it. His idea in the poem is that four men are visited by Death, but don't know who he is. He has used the poetic form to give shape to his thoughts, to help him *perform* his idea.

The section which follows outlines some forms and poetic ideas for you to try.

IDEAS FOR WRITING

Many of these ideas take the form of verbal games. Some will perhaps give you ideas for how to express what you already want to write about. Other ideas, e.g. haiku or writing a poem around a metaphor or simile are discussed in chapter 11 'Just a few lines' and in chapter 13 'New world, new forms'.

Ballads The traditional ballad form is often borrowed with successful results. Ballads tell a story, keep a regular length and rhyme pattern, generally four lines per verse. They include a large amount of dialogue, and often lead to a tragic end.

> 'Oh, where have you been, my long, long love
> This long seven years and more?'
> 'Oh, I've come to seek my former vows
> Ye granted me before.'
>
> 'Oh, do not speak of your former vows
> For they will breed sad strife;
> Oh, do not speak of your former vows
> For I have become a wife.'

Their subject matter is frequently betrayal, by a lover or a comrade, but as can be seen in Dylan's song, the form can be adapted to new concerns, or tell stories in a modern context.

Word Power

Refrain poems   Another common feature of the ballad is the use of refrains — whole lines repeated at a regular point in each verse. These are common in folk songs:

> There was a lady lived in York
> All alone and a loney
> A farmer's son he courted her
> All down the greenwood sidey.

The second and fourth lines are the same in every verse. W.B. Yeats uses the enigmatic line 'Daybreak and a candle-end' as a refrain at the end of each eight-line verse in a poem about a wild old man determined to go on living notoriously. The poem on page 126 uses the line 'The rain fell hard, the mines, the dead' at the end of each verse. Used well, a refrain can reinforce the emotion of a poem with great effectiveness.

Telling a story   There are of course lots of different ways to tell a story in a poem. These are just three.

a) Through a series of telegrams or postcards in which the reader has to 'read between the lines' to find out what is really going on. A young woman writes to her boyfriend, and we gradually guess that something is being concealed; an explorer sends cables home which become increasingly bizarre; a soldier abroad begins to change his mind about what he is doing there. You could adopt the form:

> 'His first postcard read . . .
> His second postcard read . . .'

b) Through dialogue, as often in ballad forms. This is very good for creating suspense, when one of the speakers becomes increasingly anxious while the other remains calm.

c) Through monologue, where a character tells the story. It may become evident to the reader after a while that the character's view of things is not perhaps a sympathetic one.

Contrast poems   Simple poems built on contrasts, using forms like (and of course these can be used ironically or in a bizarre way):

> I used to be . . . but now I'm . . .
> Yesterday is . . . tomorrow . . .
> What I like about x is . . . what I hate about y is . . .

Acrostics   These provide a structure which at its simplest level is an entertaining verbal game, but which can also be an exercise in wit or satire. The letters of a word are spelt in capitals down the page. Each line of the poem has to begin with that letter and say something about the subject. This is by a Junior school child:

> Catalogue —
> As you know,
> This has
> Articles listed in it.
> Looking for something?
> Oh, then look in this book.
> Good for you, there is everything here.
> Uncertain? Trust us.
> Everything O.K?

How about BUREAUCRACY or ADULTERY or POSSESS-IVENESS?

Echo poems   A form used by George Herbert in the seventeenth century in which every other line consists merely of an echo of the last part of the previous one. The sound must be the same, but the spelling, and therefore the meaning, may be different. In Herbert's poem, the echo emerges as the voice of God:

> O who will show me those delights on high?
>   *Echo*: I.
> Thou, Echo, thou art mortal, all men know
>   *Echo*: No . . .
> Then tell me, what is that supreme delight?
>   *Echo:* Light
> Light to the mind: what shall the will enjoy?
>   *Echo*: Joy

Personification This means, simply, depicting something abstract, like love or spring or time, as a human being. A battle between two personified things — war/peace, love/jealousy, sleeping/waking, could provide you with the basic structure for a lively poem, particularly if you give them rather unconventional attributes.

13 New worlds, new forms

The twentieth century has seen an extraordinary amount of experimentation and seeking out of new forms in writing, as has happened with all the arts. As a teacher of creative writing I was frequently faced with students' demands for explanations of, and introductions to, concrete poetry, free verse, stream-of-consciousness fiction, absurd theatre, imagism, the 'new novel', 'found poetry', etc. It can all be quite confusing, and might either make you back away from anything which isn't familiar and traditional, or, equally bad, make you feel a has-been because you're working hard on trying to write a few 'straight' short stories. Although not all these questions can fruitfully be dealt with in one chapter, it should be interesting to have a look at a few of the ways that writers, and students of creative writing, have experimented with new forms of poetry and prose, as there is much enjoyment and stimulus to be got out of such activity and a lot of curiosity waiting to be satisfied.

I don't propose here to start speculating about why this has happened. It is put down to anything from the decline of religion to the invention of the camera, and there's truth in both those and anything in between. Of course, artistic forms have always been changing, but never quite so fast, nor so diversely, as in our century. Perhaps we can limit ourselves to isolating three broad, and of course interlinked, areas of change. First, the development of interest, prompted largely by the growth of depth-psychology, in the mysterious workings of the mind. This focused attention sometimes on the group but much more concentratedly on the individual, his motivations and the complexities of his moment-by-moment existence. While George Eliot's *Middlemarch*, published in 1871, deals with a whole community over a period of years, James Joyce's *Ulysses*, published in 1922, even more massive in length, covers one day in the life of two individuals.

Secondly, as traditional certainties about morality, religion, society, began to crumble, it was inevitable that traditional art forms, which for so long had expressed those certainties, should be challenged too. The whole value of art and its purpose in society was thrown into question. The twentieth century is the age of artistic 'movements', all of which had differing ideas about what art should be. Writers became more self-conscious, and freer in their attitudes towards language. Writers in the nineteenth century had been at pains to reflect the realistic feel of living, and novels in particular reflected this. Their successors in the twentieth century wondered whether there might not be a deeper level of reality which could best be reached by different means. Why should dialogue in a play sound like ordinary speech and the play itself reach a satisfactory conclusion? Why should the plot of a novel follow chronological sequence if important things could be explored by overturning it? Why should poems be locked in the same mould as those of the century before?

Finally, the enormous impact of modern technology upon society was bound to be reflected in the things people wrote. Literature borrowed from the cinema in particular in its techniques, and at the same time reflected an increasingly technology-dominated world.

All this is not only extremely superficial, but may also appear irrelevant to the general purpose of this book. It is likely, however, that readers coming for the first time to a page of James Joyce, for instance, or an e e cummings poem, are likely to be merely baffled or bored if they have no idea what to expect. The categories I've divided the material into are quite arbitrary, and there's bound to be some overlap with other chapters. But this is inevitable. The dividing line between 'orthodox' and 'unorthodox' is bound to be unclear.

Playing with shapes

The idea behind a 'shape poem' or 'concrete poetry' (the two are not necessarily the same) is not, as it happens, particularly new. In the early seventeenth century, the religious poet George Herbert wrote a poem called 'Easter Wings' in which the poem was printed on the page in the shape of a bird with outstretched wings. More recently, 'shape poems' have appeared in the form of wheels, stars, snakes, faces, and so on. This itself is quite fun, and children especially usually enjoy it. But after a couple you're tempted to ask what is gained in poetic terms by writing down your snake poem in the shape of a snake. Is the poem itself, its 'meaning', improved or even affected by the mould it's being squeezed into? Frequently not. But there are more things you can do by tinkering around with the conventional typography (the way a piece of writing is arranged on the paper) of a poem. This is by the Liverpool poet Roger McGough:

40 –	LOVE
middle	aged
couple	playing
ten	nis
when	the
game	ends
and	they
go	home
the	net
will	still
be	be
tween	them

Here the poem not only develops the fairly common idea of the ball game:

Ping	Pong
Ping	Pong
Ping	SMASH

— but develops it to make a wry comment on the relationship between the two players.

Still within the definition of a 'shape poem', here's one by a student of mine:

'The lover of the nile'

Beginning
at the
mouth,
he lingers,
between
the

138

Pyramids
then slowly
continues,
till,
 passing
  over
   the
        mount,
          he
          finds
          himself
          in
        the
      Valley
    of the
  Kings.
Basking
in the
warmth,
he
languorously
  explores each
              bank,
            then
            with
          a
        sudden
        thrust
          surges
          up
          the
          Nile,
          until
          he ends
      his
    journey
    spent,
      in
      the
      interior,
      where
        it
        all
      began.

The typography lends much to the overall poem, not only following the winding of the river Nile, past the monuments on its banks, but also contributing to the poem's other more important feature, that of lazily and entertainingly describing love-making at the same time. The poem isn't only a visual joke, but one which exploits in a fairly elaborate way the potential of double meanings.

Both these poets, but particularly Roger McGough, rely on the overall 'shape' of the thing they're describing to give their poems impetus. We read the poem as a whole, because without the outline shape much of the effect would be lost. Words are used as bricks with which to build the whole. In the next poem, letters themselves, the bricks of the bricks, are separated out and reassembled in intriguing ways, which essentially is the difference between a shape poem and concrete poetry. This was written by the poet Edwin Morgan, for whom this kind of writing is a speciality:

'Message Clear'

```
     am                 i
                                    if
   i am                        he
         he r        o
         h      ur   t
         the re          and
         he     re     and
         he re
   a                   n    d
        th   e    r                 e
   i am      r                     ife
                      i n
              s      ion and
   i                      d     i e
     am    e res    ect
     am    e res    ection
                         o             f
          the                      life
                         o             f
       m    e             n
             sur  e
```

```
        the                 d       i e
i           s
            s    e  t    and
i am the    sur           d
  a   t   res      t
                        o          life
i am  he r                         e
i a             ct
i        r   u      n
i  m   e  e       t
i              t                i e
i          s    t    and
i am th            o      th
i am    r             a
i am the   su     n
i am the   s       on
i am the  e   rect on       e if
i am     re        n    t
i am        s       a         fe
i am      s   e    n     t
i   he e              d
i   t e  s     t
i        re        a d
  a   th re        a d
  a       s    t on          e
  a   t  re        a d
  a   th r       on          e
i         resurrect
                    a       life
i am              i  n      life
i am      resurrection
i am the resurrection and
i am
i am the resurrection and the life
```

Well, whatever's going on here the first impression is of somebody or something trying to make a statement, or more abstractly, of a statement trying to be made. Success is finally reached in the last line. I think it's a good poem because that *is* our initial impression and it's the most important one in the poem. Our effort, then, to understand is similar to the effort the 'voice' is making to be understood. You make it 'work' (it would be unfair to not to make this clear at some stage) by imagining the final sentence potentially printed in full on every line, with the poet only 'punching out' selected letters along the line, which when read straight across, make increasingly good sense:

> am i
> if
> I am he
> hero
> hurt
> there and
> here and
> there
> I am rife
> in
> sion and
> I die
> a mere sect
> a mere section
> of
> the life
> of
> men [and so on]

Finally the message becomes clear: 'I am the resurrection and the life', when the statement is read in its totality. It is as if a computer was pushing out punched cards all of which are partially right, but only completely right at the end. It could also be seen as a history of the developing power of Christ, beginning in confusion, through 'a mere sect', to 'I am the erect one, if I am rent I am safe. I am sent', to the triumph of the final statement.

Playing with words

That last poem was as much 'playing with words' as 'playing with shapes'. And there's a sense in which all creative writing is 'playing with words'. But I am here more concerned with a particular kind of word-play in which new words are invented, or old ones used in an unconventional way, or old words are put together to make new ones.

There is one famous instance of a style in which words are consciously always doing several things at a time, and that's James Joyce's *Finnegans Wake*, published in 1939. This large book seems to be one night's dream sequence of a Dublin tavern keeper as portrayed by the stream of his consciousness. Joyce creates hundreds of 'portmanteau' words, which take elements from different words and put them together to make a single word with several meanings, and uses puns and allusions everywhere.*

> Well, you know or don't you kennet or haven't I told you every telling has a taling and that's the he and the she of it. Look, look, the dusk is growing!
> O, my back, my back, my bach! I'd want to go to Aches-les-Pains. Pingpong! There's the Belle for Sexaloitez! And Concepta de Send-us-pray! Pang! Wring out the clothes! Wring in the dew!

Here the sounds of words are manipulated in an attempt to make them extend and enrich their meanings. But however intriguing such a passage is, the drawbacks of a sustained narrative in this style are obvious. It's such heavy going. It could be satisfying only if our linguistic resources, and our patience, came close to Joyce's. Unsurprisingly, the book is more read about than read.

*Joyce's daughter Lisa was becoming schizophrenic at the time that he was writing the book. He took her to see the psychoanalyst Jung, convinced that his daughter's schizophrenic word games were no different from his own. 'You are both going to the bottom of the river' Jung told him 'but she is falling and you are diving.' There is certainly a similarity, though the tone is different, between Joyce's linguistic 'diving' and the way some schizophrenics describe their state of mind: 'I'm a no-un, an in-divide-you-all' (Quoted in R.D. Laing's *The Divided Self*)

Once you begin to invent new words and coin your own expressions you run the risk of either being downright unintelligible, or bogging your reader down in a linguistic swamp. Here's one instance, though, of a writer experimenting with the vocabulary of the language and being, I think, marvellously successful. It's taken from the beginning of Anthony Burgess's *A Clockwork Orange*, set some time in the not very distant future:

'What's it going to be then, eh?'

There was me, that is Alex, and my three droogs, that is Pete, Georgie, and Dim, Dim being really dim, and we sat in the Korova Milkbar making up our rassoodocks what to do with the evening, a flip dark chill winter bastard though dry. The Korova Milkbar was a milk-plus mesto, and you may, O my brothers, have forgotten what these mestos were like, things changing so skorry these days and everybody very quick to forget, newspapers not being read much neither. Well, what they sold there was milk plus something else. They had no licence for selling liquor, but there was no law yet against prodding some of the new veshches which they used to put into the old moloko, so you could peet it with vellocet or synthemesc or drencrom or one or two other veshches which would give you a nice quiet horrorshow fifteen minutes admiring Bog And All His Holy Angels And Saints in your left shoe with lights bursting all over your mozg. Or you could peet milk with knives in it, as we used to say, and this would sharpen you up and make you ready for a bit of dirty twenty-to-one, and that was what we were peeting this evening I'm starting off the story with.

Although the vocabulary is unfamiliar, it's not impossible to decode, and quickly becomes easy to follow, because it's consistent and because it already has some connections with ordinary talk. We pick up that 'veshches' means drugs, that 'droogs' are mates, then there are the Russian-based words, which are effective in giving a sense of a Britain very different in 'feel' from now — here we have 'moloko' for milk, and 'horrorshow', a sinister blend of English with the Russian word for good, later we find 'devotchkas' for girls, 'malchicks' for boys. There are also complete phrases like 'a bit of dirty twenty-to-one' with their air of casual cruelty. The mixture of violent, futuristic slang and recognisable English creates a sense of a world that is scary and brutal, and recognisably British. Alex's way of speaking becomes anything but a swamp. It takes the reader, on the contrary, straight into the heart of the experience at the most fundamental level, that of language.

Bombs, bureaucrats, bargain buys

As we have seen, Edwin Morgan's 'computer' poems suggest possibilities of drawing on the forms of modern technology in writing. It's interesting to note that (unlike 'Message Clear') most examples of such writing turn the language and form of modern technological society back against itself in satire. The treatment of the individual in mass society, for example, is a common theme. The student who wrote the 'Love Letter' below uses that inescapable modern phenomenon, the application form.

'Love letter'

PLEASE PRINT ALL ENTRIES

		Last	First	Middle
Name in full	Mr			
Number	Street	Road	City/Town	
State		Code	Previous address, if any	
			Tel. no.	
Marital Status Married/Single/Divorced/Widowed/Separated/**Explain**				
Date of birth (Mnth Dy Yr)**Place of birth**				
In case of emergency notify			Relationship	
Ever seen me before Yes/No/Don't know **Explain**				
Names of my friends you know			Explain	
Height	Weight	**Wear glasses** Yes/No/Don't know		
Handed Left/Right/Ambidextrous **Physical defects** Yes/No/Don't know				
Explain				
		Education		
School		Marks obtained at O or CSE level		
College		Marks obtained		

145

Word Power

Habits	
Reading Yes/No **Explain**	Literature/Light Romantic/ Historical/
Psychological/Magazines/Pornography/Newspapers/Can't Read	
Sports Yes/No **Explain**	Cricket/Football/Hockey/Table Tennis
Golf/Tennis/Never Selected	
Films Yes/No/ **Explain**	(Art/Musicals/Formula/Suspense/
Crime/Happy Endings)	**(No. of films seen per month)**
Skills	
Number of girls been with	**Explain**
Like taking them out Yes/No	**(Dinner/Concert/Films)**
Hold hands while walking Yes/No **Explain**	
Kiss Yes/No **Explain**	(Good-Night/Birthday/Otherwise)
How long do you expect the relationship to continue Few months/	
Less than that/Few Years/More than that/**Forever**	
Do you like me/respect me **find me** Attractive/Worth being with/Beautiful	

It is agreed and understood that false statements, if any, on this form may be considered sufficient ground for the termination of the relationship, as soon as discovered.

Signature/Thumb impression

Although there are one or two inconsistencies in the questions being asked (It's not entirely clear whether the person who is filling it in has ever met the person who is to receive it), the idea is a good one. It's entertaining, and salutory, to see in action something as impersonal as an application form trying to get its teeth round the delicacies of an emotional relationship. The very fact that it should take this task upon itself in the first place is of course the basis of the satire.

The emotionally stunted world of market research is again held up for scrutiny by the contemporary English poet Peter Porter, in a rather more elaborate and scathing way, again using a characteristic feature of modern society to make its point. The poem is called 'A Consumer's Report', and although the thoughts are continuous, they can also be seen as successive answers to a manufacturer's questionnaire:

146

'A Consumer's Report'

The name of the product I tested is Life,
I have completed the form you sent me
And understand that my answers are confidential.
I had it as a gift
I didn't feel much while using it,
In fact I think I'd have liked to be more excited.
It seemed gentle on the hands
but left an embarrassing deposit behind.
It was not economical
and I have used much more than I thought
(I suppose I have about half left
but it's difficult to tell) —
although the instructions are fairly large
there are so many of them
I don't know which to follow, especially
as they seem to contradict each other.
I'm not sure such a thing
should be put in the way of children —
It's difficult to think of a purpose
for it. One of my friends says
it's just to keep its maker in a job.
Also the price is much too high.
Things are piling up so fast,
after all, the world got by
for a thousand million years
without this, do we need it now?
(Incidentally, please ask your man
to stop calling me 'the respondent',
I don't like the sound of it)
There seems to be a lot of different labels,
sizes and colours should be uniform,
the shape is awkward, it's waterproof
but not heat resistant, it doesn't keep
yet it's very difficult to get rid of
whenever they make it cheaper they seem
to put less in — if you say you don't
want it, then it's delivered anyway.
I'd agree it's a popular product,
it's got into the language; people
even say they're on the side of it.

> Personally I think it's overdone,
> a small thing people are ready
> to behave badly about. I think
> we should take it for granted. If its
> experts are called philosophers or market
> researchers or historians, we shouldn't
> care. We are the consumers and the last
> law makers. So finally, I'd buy it.
> But the question of a 'best buy'
> I'd like to leave until I get
> the competitive product you said you'd send.

There's not *only* humour in the way that everything the consumer says about life can be applied to any consumer product like soap powder — there's also a nasty feeling, stronger towards the end of the poem, that the consumer is so thoroughly brainwashed by advertising that he or she really does look at life as if it were no more than a commodity, ideally wipe-clean and hygienic, designed for eye-appeal and quick disposability. It's a satire on the whole consumer mentality.

That mentality is an essentially passive one, cowardly even, in its refusal to face up to ugliness and suffering, and the twentieth century is remarkable for having developed an ability to obscure unpleasant or inhuman facts with abstract or cosy language. This is the language of propaganda, whether of the advertiser or the politician. The public relations element is deep in all of us now. We call a new way of doing maths in schools SMILE (Schools Mathematics Individualised Learning Experiment), we call genocide 'pacification', and forced marches 'relocation of personnel'. It can be comic, or sinister. Writers haven't been slow to respond to this, notably George Orwell whose essay 'Politics and the English Language' is full of excellent advice about writing in general. One student of mine came up with this original idea, an extract from a manual on 'Civil Defence'.

'Civil Defence Manual'

In the event of enemy action
Preparation is of vital importance.
This manual has been prepared
With just such a contingency in mind.

In case you have been hit from behind
(while enjoying the sunset etc.)
We will use the key word 'SMILE'
S — Stop bleeding by applying direct pressure
        or cold compress.
M — Maintain body temperature by wrapping yourself
        in a blanket (if possible, induce a vacuum)
I — Imbibe emetics in case of poison in the system
        (not in case of acids)
L — Lure away danger by positive means
        (avoid being unscrupulous)
E — Either use sling or splints to guard
        against further damage.

In case of bites from Aves, Pisces, Reptilia,
Amphibia, Mammalia including Homosapiens
the following treatment is prescribed —
Wash and dab wound with antiseptic
(In case of insane mammalia/Homosapiens
ignore completely so that wound bleeds freely)
If bitten by reptilia
the size, age and sex should be determined
before applying tourniquet and incising wound
to remove all trace of venom.
For all the above cases the important
Pass word is 'Do not Panic'

The above emergency methods are not required
if following precautions are taken.
A built-in warning system should be installed.
At the least sign of 'possible enemy' approach
the alarm should be tuned to blast
Assemble at Static Mobile Post.

On receipt of instruction from Control room
or messenger, action must be taken.
The safety of crowds should be sought.
Do not turn your back on the enemy
Also do not face the enemy
Without protective, warm clothing.
Conversation if not totally absent
should be kept to the barest minimum
Do not leave any part exposed,
to protect against possible bites
If frightened, smile, say 'Good morning/afternoon/evening'
(It will help to avoid physical contact)
and be off.

This chapter has necessarily been a rag-bag of different
unorthodox ways of writing. Nor is it implied that anything
which appears in other chapters is necessarily to be described as
'orthodox'. The word 'experimental' has been stretched to cover
many things. There is a difference, for example, between the
one-off attempt to do a particular thing ('Love letter', *A
Clockwork Orange*) and the development of an entire prose style
suitable for the full range of experience. Joyce spent seventeen
years on *Finnegans Wake*, and said of it 'I felt I could not use
words in their ordinary connections . . . When morning comes
of course everything will be clear again . . . I'll give them back
their English language . . . .' 'Morning', however, didn't come,
and Joyce's style can be counted experimental in our terms in
that the book is now ignored except by scholars. The passages in
this chapter have been chosen to give the reader some idea of
the possibilities and, occasionally, dangers, of unorthodox
writing. My general belief is that there is a lot of enjoyment to be
had from taking chances with styles and forms for a specific
purpose. The development of a particular personal, strongly
unorthodox *style* however, is filled with dangers of imitation,
obscurity and pretentiousness, dangers which only a few writers
manage to overcome to make their style really work for them.
What the reader finds appealing or stimulating here will have to
be, as usual, a matter of personal choice.

IDEAS FOR WRITING

A noise poem: describe an experience or an activity solely in terms of the noises made during it, by people or things (e.g. riding a horse, a thunderstorm breaking, a man trying to start a car).

Break the conventions of everyday language and try a piece of experimental prose describing a particular violent or ecstatic experience. Do anything you like with punctuation, spelling, layout, etc.

A twentieth century manual on murder, carefully written in a language that smoothes over the nature of the facts being discussed. Or, in the same vein, a twentieth century marriage contract.

The government probably has a taped radio announcement ready to play to calm the population in the event of a nuclear war. Write your version of that radio announcement.

Two modern lovers go through a 48-hour crisis in their relationship by sending a rapid series of telegrams to each other. Write those telegrams.

Pages from a diary of the future. Sketch some details of everyday life in the twenty-first century, remembering that the language will have gone through some changes by then.

Computer-designed love letters and christmas cards. Alternatively, write a series of letters between a human being trying to redress some fault, and the computer who deals with his letters.

A series of glossy, consumer magazine advertisements, which exploit the methods and language of modern techniques of persuasion, for tanks, nerve gas, nuclear shelters . . . or even an abstract thing like love, or religion.

Take a historic sentence and use it as the basis for a concrete poem. Experiment with the typography and layout for different effects (see 'Message Clear' on pp. 140-141). For example:

Poets are the unacknowledged legislators of the world
Laugh and the world laughs with you
Let him who is without sin cast the first stone.

14 A bit of drama

Setting up situations

A sixteen year old school kid surprises a male and a female teacher kissing in a stockroom in which he has left his motorcycle. The ill-feeling that arises leads to him holding a lighted cigarette over the petrol tank and keeping them, and himself, prisoners . . .

(*Gotcha* by Barrie Keefe)

A man in a New York park falls into conversation with another man on a bench. He tells him at length about the difficulties he has with a ferocious dog who inhabits the stairs up to his flat, and the complex measures he takes to defeat, or win round, the dog . . .

(*Zoo Story* by Edward Albee)

Two identically dressed men with despatch cases meet on an empty stage and exchange crazily jumbled clichés of patriotism and diplomacy. They sign pieces of paper, then tear bits off them, becoming increasingly angry, then manic, as they dance around the stage like schoolboys, making noises of gunfire . . .

(*Out of the Flying Pan* by David Campton)

Some young people are at a party. Suddenly the lights fuse, and they are left in darkness. (How this works on stage is described later). The power does not return for some time. Needless to say, they don't sit in silence waiting.

(*Black Comedy* by Peter Shaffer)

A man and a woman sit facing each other. She is worried by something, he takes a rather patronising interest. But what is it she is worried by?

she: I can't help it.
he : Can't help what?
she: Getting into this.
he : Getting into what?

Word Power

she: If I could say I wouldn't be in it.
he :   What's it like?
she: It's terrible.
he :   In what way?
she: I can't say. That's why it's so terrible . . .
(Adapted from *Do You Love Me?* by R.D. Laing)

The curtain goes up and the audience is confronted with another audience opposite them watching a stage, on which the body of a man lies sprawled over the settee. A man in the audience noisily rustles his programme, another eats a box of chocolates — theatre critics. They begin to chat . . .

(The Real Inspector Hound by Tom Stoppard)

All of these situations have provided the basis for good pieces of modern drama. The shortest, the dialogue which begins 'I can't help it', lasts about seven minutes; the longest, Peter Shaffer's *Black Comedy*, lasts around an hour. While *Out of the Flying Pan* is circular, ending as it begins, *The Real Inspector Hound* is a bizarre, complicated whodunnit involving the theatre critics themselves. None of these is a conventional, realistic, two-hour, three act, half-a-dozen characters kind of play. Whatever each of the playwrights chooses to 'do' with the subject matter, the situations themselves provide an immediate interest, whether through an instantly felt tension or a curiosity at the unusual spectacle on the stage.

In a conventional full-length play, it is generally character (what the figures on the stage are like as people), and plot (the story in which they all play a part) which provide the main interest for the audience. This is not wholly true of the plays described above however, and need not be true at all. This chapter, in fact, isn't about writing *plays*, if by a play we mean something that realistically tells a story in about two hours, which is in itself a very limited definition. Besides, it's very difficult to keep an audience interested in watching half a dozen people talk to, or even murder, each other for a couple of hours. It might be more useful to describe a play as a 'piece of drama over (say) five minutes long, needing one or more people to act it, in front of one or more spectators'.

When children play, they do not feel the need to convince their audience (if any) that a stick with a bit of green cloth on it really *is* a dragon, or a ring of chairs really *is* a fortress, or that a

154

six year old really *is* the commander of the U.S. Cavalry. They simply accept the conventions of the game, of the play, and see what can be done with them — and that usually means, a lot. A lot not so much in terms of plot, but of performance, the fun, the excitement, the danger, that can be got out of setting up a situation.

'Setting up situations of dramatic interest' is what the playwrights whose plays are described at the beginning of the chapter have done, rather than thinking only in terms of a realistic plot with realistic characters told over two hours. This point is made not merely to encourage the inexperienced or time-starved writer to attempt some drama, but also because it is a feature of modern theatre, which has turned significantly away from realistic, full-length psychological drama towards experi-mentation. Since the early sixties, workshop theatres, travelling drama groups who play in pubs and community halls, street theatre groups, schools and colleges as well as TV and radio drama, have shown what can be done on a small scale, with a low budget, and using techniques which constantly open out our understanding of the conventions of theatre. (And as drama is above all a visual, active experience, it goes without saying that to see or hear as much as possible of this kind of drama, if only on television and radio, is essential.)

The conventions of drama

What are those conventions? The most familiar is that often known as the 'fourth wall', in which the audience looks in on, say, a sitting room, faces three of its walls on the set, and itself comprises the fourth one. The actors maintain the illusion that they are unobserved by anybody. It would be inconceivable, therefore, for any member of the cast to address the audience — this would break the spell. Nor would they speak aloud to themselves, as people do not generally do that in real life, or certainly not at any length; and the illusion of real life is essential in this kind of drama.

But of course this has not always been so in the theatre. In Shakespeare, for instance, characters very much do speak aloud to themselves (Macbeth, for example, expressing the terror in his mind before the murder of Duncan), or make asides to the audience, or introduce the play before it starts. In Medieval plays, audiences might be asked to pass judgement on the actions of a character, or listen while the moral of the story was pointed out to them. This technique, of recognising the existence of the audience, is now a fairly common part of modern drama. In John Osborne's *Luther*, the audience becomes the congregation when Luther preaches; in Trevor Griffith's *Comedians* the audience becomes at one point the clientele of a pub, before whom a group of trainee stand-up comics are put through their paces; in the plays of Bertolt Brecht, there are frequently figures who comment aloud on the action to the audience; in *Night and Day* by Tom Stoppard, one of the characters occasionally reveals her thoughts to the audience, but the other characters are unable to hear her. The effect of breaking the 'fourth wall' convention in this way can be entertaining, involving, and some playwrights would argue, more faithful to the truth of the situation: what is being presented, after all, is a play and not real life.

Another convention which we often take for granted is that the audience knows from the beginning who the characters are, and where they are. But uncertainty can be fruitful: it is important that the man and woman in R.D. Laing's 'I can't help it' are nameless, generalised, non-realistic, that they are typical of all of us and the knots we tie ourselves into. In David Storey's *Home*, we listen to the conversation of the two main characters for some time before we become aware that the setting is a mental home. Had we been aware of this from the start, we would undoubtedly have been tempted to distance ourselves from the characters, to categorise them as mentally ill and therefore different. This device also ironically undermines the question of 'what is real', of obvious relevance in a play about a mental home. At the beginning of the short play *The Lover*, by Harold Pinter, a wife and her husband discuss the wife's lover. In the next scene, the husband is out and the lover enters. The lover is played by the same actor who has played the husband. With the same people playing the wife/mistress and the husband/lover, the business of role playing naturally comes under scrutiny as the play progresses. They are after all the same people, only in different roles.

The breaking of the conventions of realism in this way creates numerous possibilities, and is especially suited to brief, experimental drama. While the next two devices are taken from longer plays, both are theatrical 'tricks' which would work well in a shorter piece. In the previously mentioned *Black Comedy*, the stage opens in darkness but we hear the sound of drinks being poured and the chatter of party conversation; the record player then dribbles to a halt to signify a power cut, so the lights come up and the characters begin to grope around as if they were in complete darkness. The trick is wholly convincing, and delightful to watch. There is a similar reversal, this time with language, in Brian Friel's *Translations*, in which the Irish characters are portrayed speaking only Irish, though they in fact speak English on stage, and the English only English. The audience is thus able to understand what both sides are saying, while the characters understand only what is spoken in their own tongue. There is even a love scene between a young Englishman and an Irish girl, in which neither of them can understand a word the other speaks, and yet manage to communicate and express their own rapture in an extraordinarily moving way. While this is a device, it is not merely a gimmick: one of the main concerns of the play is the way that language unites and divides human beings.

Situations which are of immediate dramatic interest, however, are not created only by tinkering with theatrical convention, or by abandoning realism. Any situation of tension or conflict which needs no painstaking build-up (the discovery of somebody doing wrong, a husband and wife waiting outside a divorce court) will serve as potential material for a short play. The theatrical potential of explosive situations is exploited by the many playwrights who use theatre for political purposes. They are less concerned with depicting the complexities of personal relationships, or playing games with theatre itself, than with a bold presentation of aspects of conflicts and contradictions in society. Barrie Keefe, for example, in the short play mentioned earlier, *Gotcha*, uses the boy holding the cigarette over the petrol tank to express responses to modern education which are not intended to be seen as the moanings of one particular rejected individual, but as a condemnation of society's values.

In a slightly longer play, *Mama Dragon*, Farrukh Dhondy analyses different attitudes to black unrest, from those of liberal white social worker, and fake-radical black girl who sleeps with him, through bottle-throwing aimless young blacks, to organised guerilla violence. The setting is a community club in Brixton around the time of a proposed National Front march. The dramatic tension is created by the arrival of an older black youth who has finished his stint with the army in Northern Ireland, where he has learnt the techniques of street warfare, and stolen a deadly flame thrower, a 'mama dragon'. The dramatic question 'will he use it?' is linked to the moral and political one of his justification for doing so.

Both *Gotcha* and *Mama Dragon*, then, quickly set up situations which are dramatically and politically explosive. In both plays the audience forms a 'fourth wall'. Both plays are straightforwardly realistic. Dhondy's play, however, also features songs by a reggae group at the edge of the stage, which are woven into the narrative. In the same way, much theatre which unashamedly sets out to preach a message uses music, dance, mime and so on, as if to announce 'We're not going to pretend that we're not trying to teach you something, so we might as well make it as entertaining and interesting a lesson as possible'. Joan Littlewood's *Oh, What a Lovely War*, a satire on the First World War, strings together songs from the trenches and music halls, speeches of Earl Haig's, casualty statistics, sketches of international tycoons shooting wildfowl and discussing the profits of the arms trade, and so on. The audience is presented with continuous novelty and ingenuity, a variety-show freshness, but the humour is often dark, the message bitter.

What kind of dialogue?

So far in this chapter the emphasis has been on ways of thinking about drama generally, other than in terms of straightforward realistic plays. This is not the place to touch upon the vast area of mime, or improvisation, or working with sound and light effects, all of which can help to make a dramatic experience. But there remains, for the writer at least, whatever the techniques chosen to achieve the results desired, the central question of dialogue. While this is certainly crucial, it has been left till last because writing dialogue cannot be discussed in isolation from the question of the 'style' of the piece of drama. Put simply, the considerations of writing realistic dialogue are not necessarily the same as those of writing dialogue for a more experimental piece. What follows, then, are examples and discussion of dialogue written in different styles, written in progressively less realistic modes. As ever, there are no iron rules about writing dialogue, but a few useful points may arise in the course of discussion.

The scene is an interview room in a police station on general election night. Karn, a detective, has been listening to results on the telephone, looking forward to the Thatcherite 'new dawn'. He is waiting to see a black suspect, Delroy, whose wife has been found bleeding to death in their flat while Delroy was in the pub. Delroy has not mentioned his wife's death, and we learn later that he is quite unaware that anything has happened to her. Wilby, the detective constable, has told Karn that Delroy believes he is there on 'sus', on 'suspicion'.

He replaces receiver. WILBY enters with DELROY. Pause.

Delroy: We ain't been introduced. My name is Leon Delroy.

Karn: How very civilised Mr Delroy. How very nice to make your acquaintance. D.C. Wilby and me, D.S. Karn.

Delroy: Well, well — this is a nice room. I haven't been in this room before.

Karn: Décor's quite simple. Let me show you around. We've gone in for the hardwearing but easy to clean.

Delroy: Do you get a lot of mess in here then?

Karn: You never can tell.

Delroy: Very nice. Very, um, simple.

Karn: Same with the furniture. I trust you approve?

Delroy: Well I . . . What did you say your name was?

Karn: Karn. K A R N.

Delroy: Is that German or something?

Karn: It's my father's name. His father gave it to him and he gave it to me. Sort of family heirloom.

Delroy: Nice.

Karn: Handed down from generation to generation. All English. Pure stock.

Delroy: Well, this looks the most comfortable chair.

Karn: Then sit down, do sit down Mister Delroy. Take the weight off your feet. How long did you say you were in the boozer?

Delroy: From about sevenish.

Karn: More than three hours solid boozing! Then my gawdfathers, you must be fucking worn out Mister Delroy. I do apologise. Perhaps, Wilby, you could bring in a chaise-longue to make Mister Delroy here a bit more comfortable.

Delroy: You're too kind, Mister Karn, but this'll do. As it happens, I haven't got too much time to spare tonight. I'm in a bit of a hurry. We're going down to the club to watch the election results.

Karn: The club, eh? What one's that? Beefsteak? Brooks? White's or the M.C.C.?

Delroy (*laughing*): I ain't fussy.

Karn: That's nice to hear.

Delroy: As it happens, Working Men's Club. But if you was thinking of inviting me to one of them —

(from *Sus*, by Barrie Keefe)

The audience is being asked to believe that these are three real people in a real situation. Accordingly the characters say nothing that a hard white policeman and a young black man might not say in real life. Good realistic dialogue, like this, has to capture the audience's interest, convey information, reveal characters, develop a situation, all at the same time. To do this, Barrie Keefe creates an atmosphere of light-hearted combat between the two men, played out at the level of wit . . . at least in Delroy's case it is light-hearted. Karn's has a sour, menacing edge to it:

Delroy: Well, well — this is a nice room. I haven't been in this room before.

Karn: Décor's quite simple. Let me show you around. We've gone in for the hard-wearing but easy to clean.

Delroy: Do you get a lot of mess in here then?

Karn: You never can tell.

The apparent good humour of Karn's remarks about his name being passed down as a 'sort of family heirloom' is belied when he continues with a hint of menace to his black suspect, 'Handed down from generation to generation. All English. Pure stock'. A dramatically tense moment. Delroy chooses to ignore the remark. The audience cannot. If there is any one rule of dialogue it is that of economy: nothing that anybody says should be superfluous or repetitive, but should serve to move the play forward, whether in terms of action, ideas, character, information, tension.

One of the reasons why this dialogue is interesting to listen to is that both characters have a natural wit, an instinctive way of fencing with words, particularly in a sarcastic way. Anybody writing realistic dialogue, however, has to come up against the fact that many people are inarticulate and do not find words coming readily and interestingly to them. You can end up writing dialogue which reflects this, and which is thereby wholly 'true-to-life', but which could have the audience shifting impatiently in their seats and wholly losing interest in characters who are coming across simply as boring people with nothing to say to each other. As with any kind of dialogue, in prose fiction too, it is never enough simply to let two 'ordinary' people talk to each other and call it realism. Not all realistic dialogues (like those in real life, for instance) are interesting to listen to. Frequently a compromise is reached in stage dialogue: the majority of characters in such plays are in fact rather more articulate than people are in reality, if not in terms of unlikely vocabulary, then in terms of wit, or the imagery of their speech, or its rhythms: a measure of 'unrealism' acceptable in return for lively dialogue.

An odd *feel* of realism, in dialogue that is in fact quite extraordinary, can be found in the next exchange, between an old tramp, Jenkins, who has been surprised by Mick going through Mick's brother's things in their dingy flat.

Mick: What's your name?
Davies: I don't know you. I don't know who you are.
      Pause.
Mick: Eh?
Davies: Jenkins.
Mick: Jenkins?
Davies: Yes.
Mick: Jen . . . kins.
      Pause.
   You sleep here last night?
Davies: Yes.
Mick: Sleep well?
Davies: Yes.

161

> *Mick*: I'm awfully glad. It's awfully nice to meet you.
>   *Pause.*
>   What did you say your name was?
> *Davies*: Jenkins.
> *Mick*: I beg your pardon?
> *Davies*: Jenkins!
>   *Pause.*
> *Mick*: Jen . . . kins.
>   *A drip sounds in the bucket. DAVIES looks up.*
> You remind me of my uncle's brother. He was always on
> the move, that man. Never without his passport. Had an
> eye for the girls. Very much your build. Bit of an athlete.
> Long-jump specialist. He had a habit of demonstrating
> different run-ups in the drawing-room round about
> Christmas time. Had a penchant for nuts. That's what it
> was. Nothing else but a penchant. Couldn't eat enough of
> them. Peanuts, walnuts, brazil nuts, monkey nuts, wouldn't
> touch a piece of fruit cake. Had a marvellous stop-watch.
> Picked it up in Hong Kong. The day after they chucked
> him out of the Salvation Army. Used to go in number four
> for Beckenham Reserves. That was before he got his Gold
> Medal. Had a funny habit of carrying his fiddle on his back.
> Like a papoose. I think there was a bit of the Red Indian in
> him. To be honest, I've never made out how he came to be
> my uncle's brother. I've often thought that maybe it was the
> other way round. I mean that my uncle was his brother and
> he was my uncle. But I never called him uncle. As a matter
> of fact I called him Sid. My mother called him Sid too. It
> was a funny business. Your spitting image he was. Married
> a Chinaman and went to Jamaica.
>   *Pause.*
> I hope you slept well last night.

(from *The Caretaker* by Harold Pinter)

Again, there's little here that, in theory at least, an ordinary
man like Mick couldn't say, no grand phrases, no long words, no
poetry. In fact though, and the effect is dramatically very
powerful, Mick's way of speaking is bizarre and frightening. It's
bizarre because he chooses to tell the extraordinary story of his
'uncle's brother' at such a time, and frightening because his

motive for doing so, in this utterly confident delivery, must remain unknown to Davies and the audience. It gives a wierd sense of total, and ruthless, control. There is even something studiedly cruel about the way he tosses in words like 'penchant' and 'papoose', words which would be quite unfamiliar to Davies. On top of all this, it's also darkly funny: the details of the story itself make no sense at all ('I think there was a lot of Red Indian in him . . . Married a Chinaman and went to Jamaica'), and Mick's self-congratulatory way with words ('Nothing else but a penchant') is comic in the way that all show-offs are comic. But he's also a bully, and Davies isn't laughing. Characters in Pinter's plays, and this is a feature of much modern drama, use words to conceal what they mean just as much as to reveal it. And while on the *surface* the dialogue in the extract from *Sus* does not greatly differ from the dialogue here, the characters in the play do at least say what they mean.

The final extract begins to move resolutely away from realism, away from the pretence that what the audience is watching is real, towards the feel of an 'act' being presented to the audience. This is taken from a brief satirical sketch on modern statesmanship, performed at an Aldermaston rally. The feel of the 'double-act' is strengthened by the intentional absurdity of much of the dialogue. Two men, A and B, meet on stage. They carry briefcases. The sound of departing aircraft suggests a remote airfield. They shake hands.

B [*orating*]:   This is a hysterical evasion. I come daring the olive. Branch. Our signatures on the Charter will ensure that between our two hate stations will be established a bite of peas, to be enjoyed by our childrens, and our childrens and our childrens — and our childrens. My country devours nothing but peas, will never devour anything but peas, has never devoured anything but peas. Success crown our forts. Piece of Fiendship.

[*He steps back to the sound of applause. He indicates to A that the floor is his. A steps forward, and clears his throat*]

A speaks, spouting the same kind of nonsense. Then:

B: Over?
A: Done.

B: Business?
A: Business.
      [*A and B each bring a chair into the centre of the stage, and sit facing each other*]
A: Chairman?
B: Chairman.
      [*A stands up*]
A: Open.

      [*He smiles at B, and sits again. They smile at each other, and take sheafs of documents from their despatch-cases. Frowning, they hand documents to each other*]
      Section A, paragraph B.
B: Sentence Y, Segment C.
A: Portion U.
B: Caution D.
A: One for you.
B: Another for me.
A: Afterthought I.
B: Compromise E.
A: Page in Code.
B: Here's the key.
A: Postscript W.
B: Exhibit G.
A: A two-hour session, and we break for tea.
B: Clause P.
A: Memo three.
B: Division two.
A: Revision V.
B: B.
A: C.
B: D.
A: E.
B: G.
A: P.
B: Tea.
A:⎫ I.T.V.
B:⎬ B.B.C.

[*Each now has the other's pile of papers. They stuff them into their despatch-cases again*]
A: Yes?
B: Yes.

164

A: Then nothing remains to disturb our complete agree-
ment, and without further ado I shall produce the Treaty.
B: Since nothing remains to disrobe our complete greed-
ment, without further ago you may produce the treat. He.
A: The Charter.
B: The Barter.
A: The Carter.
B: The Garter.
A: Legato.
B: Regatta.
[*A produces an ornate document with seals dangling*]
B: Check?
A: Check.

(from *Out of the Flying Pan* by David Campton)

The distortion of the language of diplomacy ('Our country
devours nothing but peas' etc.) is designed to emphasise its
emptiness, as if they can say what they like because it doesn't
mean anything and nobody's taking any notice anyway. The
treaty signing is broken off with predictable moral indignation
and insults, and world war ensues. Not particularly difficult to
write, but an effective idea, and good to watch.

Obviously, most of the appeal lies in the tricks with language:
it would be impossible to maintain this over a longer period. The
non-realistic nature of the dialogue in Samuel Beckett's full-
length modern classic *Waiting for Godot* makes it a hard play for
some people to enjoy from start to finish. But, to repeat the point
made at the opening of the chapter, there are many possibilities
open to anyone who wishes to try their hand at drama which falls
outside the limitations of the full-length play. All that is needed
is a few ideas, and the energy to try them out.

Some suggestions follow on the next page.

IDEAS FOR WRITING

These are 'situations for drama' rather than 'plots for plays'.

A group of ventriloquists and their dummies (played by real people) sit in a waiting room before auditions with an agent. The ventriloquists talk to each other about their acts. The dummies are also able to talk to each other, 'unheard' by the ventriloquists, whom they discuss with some liveliness.

A youth club. An ex-member arrives, on the run from the police (it could be uncertain as to whether they are innocent or guilty). There is disagreement among the members as to whether they should shelter the fugitive, and what part if any the youth worker(s) should take.

A child is visited by the ghost of one of his (or her) idols — a figure from history, a dead sports star, a comic book hero. The ghost accompanies him through various scenes, with his family, girlfriend, at school, making comments, offering lighthearted advice, talking to and listening to the child. Their conversation, of course, can be heard by the audience, but not by the other characters.

In Tom Stoppard's play *After Magritte*, the curtain opens on a stage which looks like a scene from a modern painting: a man stands wearing green rubber fishing waders and little else, a lampshade hangs on a pulley balanced by a fruit filled basket, and an old woman lies on an ironing-board, furniture is jammed up against the door. The play then proceeds entertainingly to account for all this, and ends with another bizarre 'picture'. This is an idea that can be fruitfully adapted, with quite different situations. It's the drama equivalent of setting out to write a short story which will include (say): a plastic Buddha, a derailed train, two sets of identical twins, an unsigned postcard from Brazil, and a consignment of polo mallets. The fun for the writer is to link them together in a coolly far-fetched way, the fun for the audience or reader to watch that being done.

A teacher and an ex-pupil meet after some years in an unexpected situation: the pupil could be a policeman apprehending a suspect, a burglar caught red-handed, a prostitute amazed (and amused) at the identity of her client, a tax-inspector interviewing an alleged tax evader. As long as the situation is somehow difficult for at least one of them, perhaps comically so, there is material for a short play.

A group of people find themselves unable to leave a space, say a dentist's waiting room, or the dining room at a dinner party, or the large lift of a department store, or the place in which they are being held hostage by a gunman who speaks little English. The reason could be mysterious — have they in fact been gathered for some purpose? Is this their last judgement? Or it could be practical — the lift has broken down and cannot be mended for some while. How will this group of perfect strangers react, and how will they pass the time? This could be anything from realistic comedy to thriller to surreal farce.

An interviewee for a job is directed to the wrong room. The interview begins. The interviewer and the interviewee become progressively more interested or puzzled by each other's view on the 'job' as the misunderstanding persists.

After the funeral of a wealthy relative, the family gathers to hear the reading of the will. Various snippets of conversation could be spotlit (hypocritical, complacent, sentimental — keep it light) while the other characters 'freeze' and are less brightly lit. Then the will is read: it contains several surprises, in its tone, in the comments the author makes about their relatives, in what it reveals about the dead person's past life, in the way they have decided to distribute their wealth. A surprise 'mystery character' appearing at the end would provide a nice dramatic climax.

Use the idea of Peter Shaffer's *Black Comedy* (itself borrowed from classical Chinese theatre: such ideas are there to be borrowed) in which all the characters 'lose' their sense of sight in a blackout. All your characters — a family at dinner, or guests at a party, or even a single pair of lovers, temporarily lose their sense of hearing. They themselves can only communicate with gestures and hand signals, but their thoughts are spoken aloud to themselves, and therefore to the audience.

A play for radio, or your own tape recorder. The advantage of this form is that you can use sounds and voices to suggest feelings, and movement of time and place. (Dylan Thomas' famous play for voices *Under Milk Wood* deals with the dreams and fantasies of a sleeping Welsh village, for instance.) An old woman sits dozing in her armchair. In her head she hears the voices of people from her past life. Or a group of children who have never met have the mysterious ability of mentally communicating with each other across the country, or across continents. They are obviously excited about their gift, but also frightened by it. What will they do with it?

Index

HANGOVER HILL

A young woman goes missing while taking a summer job in an old mining town in California's scenic Sierra Mountains. Gail Brevard and her partners are called in to investigate the case, and she decides she must go undercover in order to get to the truth of the matter. A cruel arson murder followed by an explosion at an old mine threaten Gail's life, as she and her colleague try to put all the pieces of the puzzle together and prevent further tragedy . . .

*Books by Mary Wickizer Burgess
in the Linford Mystery Library:*

THE PURPLE GLOVE MURDERS

MARY WICKIZER BURGESS

HANGOVER HILL

Complete and Unabridged

LINFORD
Leicester

First published in Great Britain

First Linford Edition
published 2015

A catalogue record for this book is available
from the British Library.

ISBN 978–1–4448–2519–0

Published by
F. A. Thorpe (Publishing)
Anstey, Leicestershire

Set by Words & Graphics Ltd.
Anstey, Leicestershire
Printed and bound in Great Britain by
T. J. International Ltd., Padstow, Cornwall

This book is printed on acid-free paper

1

The Missing Girl

Nicholas Quintaine, rising young architect, was examining some blueprints at the desk in his office overlooking the picturesque Fisherman's Wharf section of San Francisco when he heard muffled voices in the reception area. He stopped what he was doing and sat back, expecting his next appointment, but was surprised when the door opened and a young woman entered tentatively.

'Nick? I'm so sorry to barge in on you like this, but . . . I really need your help.' She moved closer to the desk and he could see she had been crying. 'I didn't know anyone else to ask . . . '

'Marilee! Whatever's wrong?' Nick got to his feet and ushered her to a comfortable seating area looking out over the scenic street below. 'It isn't your father, is it?'

Marilee Hudson was the daughter of

one of Nick's business colleagues, Art Hudson, an electrical engineer who frequently worked with Nick on his building projects. The two had become friendly over the years and Nick had often been invited to dinner at the Hudson home.

'Oh no, Nick. Dad's just fine. It's a close friend of mine. She's gone missing and I — I don't know what to do. I've tried a few things on my own with no luck. Now I've run out of options, and Dad and I thought maybe those friends of yours, you know those lawyers back in Cathcart . . . Well, you said they were very good at coming up with solutions to this sort of thing, especially the woman . . . What was her name? Gail . . . ? I thought maybe I could hire her firm to represent me and assist somehow in finding out what has happened to Sonia. Dad said he'd help with the fee.'

'You mean Gail Brevard and Conrad Osterlitz? Well, yes, they do seem to have a knack for finding answers to difficult questions. But they're attorneys, Marilee, not detectives. What would you expect them to do that you haven't already tried? I assume you've contacted the authorities and filed a missing persons report?'

'Well yes, I did try — and so did Dad. But you see, Sonia — her name is Sonia Mattingly — disappeared the first part of June while she was on her way to a summer job . . . in Cooleyville, a small mining town up in the Sierra Mountains. I called the man who had hired her, but he claims he met the bus and she wasn't on it . . . She never arrived. I also tried calling the local authorities, but the town is too small to have a police station. They have to go all the way to the sheriff's substation in Duneville about thirty miles to the east — that is, if there's any real trouble. When I called the substation, they were unwilling to look into it. They said she was an adult and unless I could prove she had actually arrived in Cooleyville as scheduled, their hands were tied.'

'Is there any possibility she changed her mind . . . didn't go to the new job after all? Does she have a boyfriend? Is there someone she might have gone off with instead for the summer?'

'Oh, no! Sonia's just not like that. I guess I should explain a little more about her. Sonia and I have been best friends since we were kids. The Mattinglys lived next door to us, and Dad and Mom were friendly with her parents. In fact, our families spent a lot of time together before they moved over to the East Bay when Mr. Mattingly retired. Sonia and I went all the way through school together, and even shared a dorm room while we were in college.

'After her parents died, she stayed on in their house in Berkeley where she teaches grammar school. She spotted this ad in one of the *Penny-Savers*, you know those free flyers they pass out in the markets. People advertise used items for sale, odd jobs, things like that. Anyway, Sonia found this ad for a temporary summer job in Cooleyville, as a caregiver in a private home. She thought it might be fun to get away from the city for a couple of months. The job was supposed to be over by the time she would have to come back to her teaching position.'

'Do you have the name of the person

who placed the ad?'

'Yes. His name is Dunlap. There was a phone number in the ad and that's who answered when I called. Dad spoke with him as well.'

'What exactly did he say when you talked to him?'

'Not much. Just that when he went to meet the bus she was supposed to be on, she never got off. He claimed he talked to the driver, but the man didn't remember anyone of her description getting on — or off — the bus.'

'And have you checked the Berkeley house?'

'Yes, I've been over there several times. She had stopped her mail and the newspaper, and had made arrangements for yard service for the two months she was likely to be gone. I talked to a couple of her neighbors, but they've all said she had told them she was planning to be away for the summer. None of them has seen her.

'I have a key to the house, and everything seemed fine inside. The refrigerator was empty and clean. She had no pets. I'll keep checking back every week . . . but it looks as if she left and planned to be away for a while.'

'Hmmm.' Nick sat in thought for a moment. 'Well, this comes at an opportune time. I'm scheduled to go back to Cathcart tomorrow to visit my uncle.' Nick was heir and advisor to his maternal uncle, Floyd Seymour, one of Cathcart's most successful entrepreneurs. 'I'll be meeting with Gail and her partners then. I'll bring this matter to their attention and see if they would be willing to take you on as a client. In the meantime, keep checking her house as you've been doing. It's always possible she just decided to do something else and will show up eventually, safe and sound.'

'I hope you're right, Nick. But honestly, Sonia would never do anything like this. I know her too well. She's trustworthy and reliable . . . and she's always been my closest friend. She would have called me if she had changed her plans . . . ' Marilee's voice wavered and her eyes glistened.

'Hang in there. I'll see what I can do.'

Nick gave her a quick hug and held the door as she departed.

But he was frowning as he turned reluctantly back to the work on his desk. This mysterious disappearance was not just a usual legal case. And he had his doubts that Gail and her colleagues would be able (or willing for that matter) to take on such a challenge.

★ ★ ★

'No! I won't hear of it!' Conrad 'Connie' Osterlitz, senior partner of the legal firm of Osterlitz and Brevard, slammed down his fist in protest then shoved his chair back from the sturdy golden oak conference table sitting squarely in the middle of the room devoted to the firm's law library.

Rising, he turned his back on his colleagues and strode to the third-floor window, where he stood for a moment gathering his thoughts as he gazed down at the busy traffic on Cathcart's main thoroughfare. To his right, in a grassy square at the end of the street, stood the somber gray edifice of the county court house. An equal distance away to his left was the gleaming façade of the Cathcart Hotel. Between these two points, the local movers and shakers scurried purposefully back and forth, conducting trials, meeting for power lunches, making things happen. He guessed this was his world now, and he had become one of them, in the few short years since he had come here from his native Arizona.

Calmer, Connie turned back to survey the people gathered around the table. Nearest to him was Nicholas Quintaine, a good friend and frequent visitor to Cathcart, where he acted as a trusted advisor to Osterlitz and Brevard's wealthiest client, Floyd Seymour. Seated next to him was Nick's cousin, Charles Walton. Charles was also an attorney and served as the firm's head of their Arizona office. The two were as different in looks and personality as night and day. Still, they had grown up almost as brothers, and got along well, in spite of the good-natured teasing that went on between them.

At the far end of the table private

investigator Hugo Goldthwaite was comfortably sprawled, sipping at a steaming cup of coffee. His father, Hugo Sr., was founder of the local detective agency the firm kept on retainer. He was bright and efficient, and invaluable when it came to technology and ingenuity. He had saved their bacon many a time in tight situations, and his loyalty to the firm was unquestioned.

Finally, Connie turned to gaze at the last person at the table and, to him, the most important. Gail Brevard was his partner in all things, and he loved her as he loved life itself. She had brought sunlight and emotion and order into his busy existence, at a time when he needed it the most. Her safety and well-being were paramount in his mind — which was why he had reacted so violently to Nick's unorthodox proposal.

Gail herself sat tranquilly, stirring her own coffee and looking reflectively down at the notes she had compiled on the yellow pad in front of her.

'Nick,' she said quietly, raising her eyes to look directly into his, 'it would be helpful if you would leave out anything but the pertinent facts — and stop making such an effort to convince us your plan is the only one that will work. Let's think this through and see if we can come up with some sort of scenario that would put your friend's mind at ease — but not jeopardize anyone, including the person she is so concerned about.'

'I admit it all sounds very far-fetched,' Nick admitted. 'But when Marilee came to me with this, she convinced me there was something terribly wrong. Her friend, Sonia, had taken this job thinking it would be fun to get out of town for the summer.'

'Did . . . does Sonia live in San Francisco also?' Charles asked.

'No. Her parents lived over in the East Bay — in Berkeley. They're deceased now, but she had inherited their old house and was still living there at the time of her disappearance. It's located not too far from the school where she is employed.'

'Is there any possibility that she just simply went somewhere else . . . got tired of the idea of working all summer and

10

left?' Charles went on. 'Was there someone she might have gone off with on a trip or cruise — instead of taking the job?'

'I asked that very question. Marilee knew Sonia quite well. They had even roomed together at one time, and Marilee said that kind of behavior was out of character for Sonia. She was — is — just a very stable and conscientious person. Marilee is convinced that Sonia would have told her if she did leave — not just go off to unknown parts without telling anyone, especially her best friend. In fact, Marilee had gone with Sonia when she purchased the bus tickets — for June 5th, to be exact. It would have taken her less than the full day to get up there, even with the change in Sacramento to a slower tour bus. Furthermore, she had promised to call Marilee from her cell phone, just as soon as she got in.'

'Have there been any attempts to track her cell phone?'

'Marilee claims she got no response at all when she tried calling the number later that evening. As if the phone had lost its charge or had been turned off. Later, when she tried to get the authorities to check its whereabouts via GPS, they refused, since Marilee did not have written permission from Sonia to do so. Marilee's father, my old friend Art Hudson, demanded that they check it as well; but apparently, unless there is a written authorization from the owner of the phone on file, there is no way legally that the GPS can be activated.'

'And illegally?' Connie looked at Hugo, their go-to guy for all things technological.

'Nope, Boss. Can't be done. You have to go through the phone companies, and by federal law they are not allowed to do that unless they receive permission from the cops. Cops won't do it, either. Not without the written release of the owner. There've been some really sad cases of people getting lost when they got off the highway, young kids even. Their families *know* they're lost, but without that legal release . . . ' His words trailed off and he shook his head.

'And what do the people who hired her

say? I assume Marilee and her father contacted them when she didn't hear from Sonia?' Charles looked up from taking his own notes.

'The man, Dunlap, who hired her claims she never showed up in Cooleyville. She just wasn't on that particular bus when he went there that afternoon to pick her up. Marilee said the plan was that Sonia would take a Greyhound bus to Sacramento, then change there for a tour bus scheduled to stop in Cooleyville. If she did get on either bus, no one at either depot remembers her.

'Of course, considering the numbers of people going in and out of those places, it is a little difficult to find potential witnesses who may have been on the same bus. Most people in those situations are just minding their own business and not keeping track of the other passengers. She would have been remembered only if something unusual had happened on the trip. And that doesn't seem to be the case.'

'Did Marilee and her father contact the local authorities?' Gail put in. 'Surely she's filed a missing persons report with them?'

'Marilee said she and Art researched the place pretty thoroughly. Actually, there aren't any 'local' authorities to speak of. There's a sheriff's substation about halfway between Cooleyville and the next largest town. But in the village itself there's only a local magistrate of sorts, apparently sort of an honorary position, and the man is semi-retired. Any legal issues have to be referred outside. My understanding is that they more or less police themselves.

'The place is so small that everyone knows everyone — and about half the town is related to the other half. They know where all the bad pennies are, and I suspect they 'handle' any problem that arises themselves. Also there is the issue that Miss Mattingly was an adult, and presumably had the right and the wherewithal to go somewhere else if she chose. Just because she didn't tell anyone, doesn't mean she has met with foul play. I'm sure that's what they're saying up there. So, no . . . I don't think there's been any official missing person investigation. I'm not even sure what jurisdiction would handle it.'

'So if there *was* anything devious going on, the perpetrator would know how to keep it covered — or might even have co-conspirators close by in the area.' Gail nodded thoughtfully. She turned to the P.I. 'Hugo, see what else you can find out from the nearest authorities . . . and what in the hell someone up there does if anyone, a child for instance, goes missing.'

He nodded, scribbling away. 'Do you want me to get started on this right now, Boss?' he asked, glancing up at Connie, who still stood at the window. 'I could at least contact the nearest sheriff's office up there — see if they kept any record of her disappearance being reported.'

'Sure, you can use the spare office. I think there's a computer hook-up in there. If not, get one of the assistants to find what you need. Might as well know what we're dealing with here.'

The rest of the people at the table took surreptitious glances at each other.

Perhaps Nick's story was beginning to interest Connie after all. They would need his full support and blessing if they were going to take Marilee on as a client and try to find her missing friend.

★   ★   ★

Charles stood up and stretched. 'So that's the plan? Should we vet it any further? And what kind of additional precautions can we take to prevent anything going wrong?' He was the practical one of the bunch, and was always concerned about logistics.

They had been at it for about two hours now, going back and forth over the details surrounding Sonia's disappearance and how they might go about finding her. Hugo had made several enquiries of the closest authorities in Duneville, about 30 miles east of Cooleyville on the main highway to Reno. They had no record of a report of a missing person of Sonia's description on file there, and the sheriff's deputy was certain they would be reluctant to undertake any kind of widespread investigation for an adult who, according to her prospective employer in Cooleyville, had never even arrived there.

'You were right by the way, Gail,' Hugo added, 'when you asked what they would do in the case of a missing child. They would get the whole community out there looking, cadaver dogs and all. But an adult? Especially a stranger? No way would they stir themselves. They just don't see it as their responsibility. In a way I can understand their reasoning. After all, we have no proof that she actually got on that bus, other than the fact Marilee saw her buy the tickets. It would be like looking for a needle in a haystack.'

'First of all,' Connie broke in, 'I *don't* want any problems like we had at Cliffside.' He nodded in Charles's direction. Charles had come close to serious harm or even losing his life in that incident. And although they had solved the mystery in the end, Connie was adamant about not putting any of their group in jeopardy if they undertook this search.

'If there is any indication that this girl has come to a bad end we need to bring in the authorities as soon as possible. After all, we don't even know her. Marilee could be completely wrong about what might have happened. The sooner we determine that she never made it to Cooleyville the better, so far as I'm concerned. And if she *did* make it to Cooleyville, and disappeared from there just as Marilee suspects . . . ' Connie concluded, and Nick shifted uncomfortably under his gaze. ' . . . If she truly has met with foul play, then we have no business mucking about with it. Better by far that we leave it in the hands of the professionals.'

'Amen to that,' breathed Gail, remembering Connie's own close call at Black Bear Lake during the Judge Winston Craig episode.

'All right, troops.' Connie stood up and nodded to each of them. 'I think we have a plan we can work with. The first thing we'll need to do is see if Mr. Dunlap still needs a caregiver. If he does, then we'll go from there. But remember, I want no slip-ups. Let's make sure we consider all the possibilities before going forward. We can't afford any mistakes in an undertaking as unpredictable as this one is liable to be.'

2

Journey to Nowhere

The old tour bus sputtered and rattled, spewing pungent gas fumes in its wake, as it made its clumsy way deep into the green-tinged foothills north of Sacramento. A plainly dressed young woman seated about halfway back left off gazing out the dusty window, then resolutely put her head back and closed her eyes, as if to sleep. Several rows behind her a man in his late thirties glanced at her from time to time, as if to reassure himself she was still there.

Eventually the rickety bus swung around a final hairpin curve and headed up a steep incline which opened up into a small intersection. 'Cooleyville!' the driver called out towards the back of the bus. 'Everybody out! There will be a 30-minute layover — enough time to pick up a snack or souvenir at the old general store or visit the tavern and the Cooley Monument. All those continuing on to Duneville and Reno should stay close in the area. All those remaining here: Thank you for riding with us — and have a good time!'

He hopped nimbly off the bus after delivering his spiel, leaving the door open behind him. He went around to the storage bin at the side of the vehicle, where he began unloading parcels and bags belonging to those staying.

A sprawling old structure with a sign over the door announcing 'General Store — Established 1857' shared a communal wall with a much smaller annex fronted by a newer, smaller sign stating that this was the 'U.S. Post Office.'

The complex was entered from the front via an ancient and splintery wooden sidewalk which meandered on up a steep incline for a block or so. On the opposite side of the street stood another old two-story brick building which housed 'The Gold Digger,' the local (and only) tavern. A sign on the front proclaimed that there were 'Rooms to Let — Upstairs.'

Next to the tavern, nestled in a small

21

grassy lot, was a monument constructed of native stone and cement honoring 'Leonard Cooley — Inventor of the Cooley Filter' which was apparently some sort of device used in mining operations to winnow out flakes of gold from muddy stream beds.

Some of the tourists were already wandering over to take a few snapshots before entering the cool, dark tavern for a quick brew.

Gail shook off her lethargy then grabbed her purse and an oversized tote which contained a small notebook-sized computer. A larger bag containing her clothes had been stashed away in the bus's luggage compartment and would be waiting for her outside. She glanced back at the man in the rear of the bus. He nodded slightly but said nothing to her as he, too, gathered his carry-ons for departure.

She made her way down the aisle with a slightly nauseated feeling, partially from the long, bouncy ride, but also because she was very uncertain of the choice she'd made to go undercover to conduct this search for the missing Sonia Mattingly. It could be a complete waste of her time and Nick's money. Still, the problem of the whereabouts of the young woman was troubling. If Marilee Hudson was correct in her fears, they might have begun this venture too late to save her friend. Gail could only hope she could solve this mystery quickly by being on the scene.

As she stood on the dusty wooden sidewalk, guarding her bags and getting her bearings, she glanced again at the man from the bus and saw he was headed across to the tavern, possibly to look into renting a room, she thought. She was startled when a hearty male voice rang out: 'Miz Norris?' A middle-aged man with a pronounced beer belly stopped in front of her.

'Yes . . . that's me,' she answered quickly. She was glad she'd thought to use her maiden name, instead of something made up at random. At least it would get her attention when someone spoke to her. 'Are you Mr. Dunlap?'

'Yes ma'am,' he replied. 'You just got the one bag?'

'Yes, and these two here,' she said, gesturing at her handbag and the tote sitting at her feet.

'Well, let's go then.' Effortlessly, he picked up the larger suitcase and flung it into the back seat of a dusty old jeep parked nearby. He made a quick swipe over the passenger seat with a grimy cloth pulled out of his pants pocket.

'All the ground around here is red, because of all the iron in it,' he explained. 'It's how you can tell there's a lot of gold and other minerals in the soil. So in the summer, when it's dry, we get all this red dust all over everything. Then when it starts raining in the fall, it turns into red mud and leaves quite a mess . . . but we're all used to it.'

He went around to the driver's side and jumped in, waiting impatiently as Gail struggled into the passenger seat while balancing her purse and tote in front of her.

She glanced around for the safety belt, but seeing he wasn't using one, shrugged and sat back as he revved the motor, flung the vehicle into low gear, and scooted up the steep hill on a two-lane badly paved road which seemed to end in a sharp curve about half a mile into the distance.

The man kept a taciturn silence, shifting briefly as they crossed a level spot, then grinding back into lower gear as the road began to climb more steeply. Gail said nothing, but glanced to one side then the other, trying to get a feel for the location. On her left was a large square building of more modern construction, possibly a grange hall or other type of public gathering spot. To her right she could just make out a large fenced yard with a manicured lawn and well-kept flower beds fronting an imposing older home half-hidden in a copse of pines.

'Who lives there?' she asked, pointing at the attractive house.

'The judge,' Dunlap said, as if no other explanation was necessary.

'Oh . . . ' she replied. 'Nice house.' The judge must be an important personage in these parts. She made a mental note to make his acquaintance as soon as possible. If he was legitimate, she might need his help or advice at some point.

As if realizing he had been remiss in his role as tour guide, Dunlap pointed ahead, again to the right, and just beyond the judge's house.

'That there's the town cemetery. Largest and oldest one between here and Nevada City. Practically in our front yard,' he added, as he geared downward once more and the little jeep gave a mighty leap straight up from the road, which curved sharply off to the left, and onto a graveled drive leading to the very top of the hill.

As they rolled to a shuddering stop in a level red dirt compound, Gail glanced back at the cemetery just down the hill.

Although the sun was shining and the myriad tombstones, of all sizes and shapes, glittered between the trees and long grasses like a field of snowy statues, a warning sting of cold air suddenly caught her off guard and she shivered. Something was not quite right here.

3

Cold Comfort

Without a word, Dunlap hopped out of the jeep, reached back and grabbed Gail's bag, and headed toward a ramshackle set of steps leading to a wooden porch fronting a large two-story, cedar-shingled monstrosity of a house which looked to be of Victorian vintage. If the siding had ever been painted, there was no trace of it now. All the wood was of a dusty brownish hue, and the windows and door-ways were outlined with yellowed enamel, long overdue for a touch-up.

At the top of the steps and to the right, a door sporting a single pane of glass at eye-level led into what was obviously an added-on section. The annex was only one story, and the wood siding wasn't quite the same as that on the original building. This newer section also featured a galvanized tin roof — an upgrade of sorts, Gail surmised — and it stretched off down the hill to the right a little ways enclosing two or three more rooms. From where she stood, she couldn't quite see the end of it, but guessed that there must be some sort of porch or deck at the very end which looked out over a steep ravine.

The most noticeable feature of the house was a wide greyish board tacked to the fascia above the front steps which painstakingly spelled out in crooked white letters the legend: 'Hangover Hill.' Someone had painstakingly painted in two small pink elephants in a crude fashion on either side of the board. Gail shook her head. Curiouser and curiouser . . .

'Come on in,' Dunlap instructed, going ahead of her and opening the door. 'I'll introduce you to everyone.'

Everyone? Gail thought. The advertisement had only mentioned Dunlap and his wife, who was presently laid up with a broken ankle and needing a temporary caregiver until she healed enough to get around on her own while Dunlap presumably was out at work.

She entered without comment and

took stock of her surroundings. The door opened into a large square room which made up the main part of the annex. It was a kitchen, steamy warm on this humid summer day, and painted a cheerful lemony yellow. Two large open windows on either side of the room were adorned with flowery curtains which fluttered in the light breeze.

The middle wall was dominated by a large cooking stove hooked up for propane gas, but also featuring a wood-burning section which serviced a time-blackened grill. A chest-type deep freeze took up the wall under the window looking out to the rear of the property, and Gail could just glimpse a thriving house garden stretching row after row, with shiny vine-ripened vegetables visible to the naked eye. An alcove held a large old-fashioned farm sink and pantry, and an older-model refrigerator wheezed away. A fifties-era vinyl-clad dinette table with several mismatched chairs stood under the other window.

Seated at the far end of the table was a wizened little man who looked to be in his 70s, wearing, in spite of the heat, a long-sleeved faded flannel shirt buttoned to the chin and wool slacks several sizes two large for him held up with an ancient pair of ragged suspenders. He was stirring a very large spoonful of sugar into a cup of very black coffee and as she entered, he looked up and met her with a toothless grin, like some demented leprechaun.

'This here's Cousin Jimmy.' Dunlap nodded towards him. 'He usually stays at his diggin's down by Oak Creek during the summer, but we let him keep a room upstairs — for when the weather's bad, or he takes a hankering to come into town. Hi-ya, Jimmy,' he added. 'This is Miz Norris. She's come to help out while June's foot is healing.'

'How do,' Jimmy said, still smiling. 'Pleased to make your acquaintance.'

'Hello, Jimmy. My name's Gail. You may call me that if you like.' Gail smiled back at him — and wondered who else would make an appearance.

'Then there's Pops,' added Dunlap. 'He's probably out messing about in the garden. He's June's Dad. We took him in about six months ago, when he got tired of the old folks' home — or they got tired of him!' Dunlap whooped at his little joke.

'Pops still gets around good and pretty much looks after himself, so we thought, why not? After all, he *is* family.'

'That's very kind of you,' Gail murmured, trying to keep track of all the new players. 'Is there anyone else I need to know about?'

'Well, just Granny. But she's off her rocker, and pretty much stays in her room.' Dunlap scratched his arm absently. 'We keep her down here on the first floor with us, so she won't get any ideas about wandering off.'

Gail swallowed hard and nodded. 'Er, where *is* your wife, Mr. Dunlap? I'd like to meet her and see if I can get started helping her.'

'Frank — you might as well call me Frank. Better if we're all on a first-name basis, don't you think? Makes things not so formal-like.' He ignored her question.

'Yes . . . Frank. And you can call me Gail, of course. Yes, that makes things a lot easier.'

'Oh, by the way, I should mention — everyone here gets up early, so you'll need to have breakfast ready by 6:30. I gotta be at work by 8, and I have a ways to travel. I'm working construction out on that new piece of freeway up the other side of U.S. 80 — you know, the back route over to Grass Valley.'

Gail didn't know, but nodded as if she did.

'Guess you can tell by all the red dust.' He gestured at the grime-coated jeep sitting in the yard. 'And we generally eat supper by 5 or 6. We all go to bed with the chickens 'round here. You don't need to worry about dinner.'

Gail assumed he meant the noon meal, which most called 'lunch'.

'Everybody fends for themselves.' Dunlap explained. 'Just be sure there's plenty of bread and sandwich meat thawed.' He gestured toward the big freezer. 'OK, if there isn't anything else, I need to get back . . .'

Gail's head was spinning. 'Wait! I didn't realize I was going to be cooking for a large . . . family, Mr. D — Frank. Your ad said nothing about cooking. I'm not sure I can . . . '

'Oh, don't worry about that. You'll catch on in no time. And the girl will help you.'

'The girl? What girl?'

'Idy!' Frank called out. 'Come out here a minute.'

The wood floor creaked in the main part of the house, and in a moment or two a girl in her late teens appeared in the doorway, a step up from the kitchen. Her brownish hair was untidy, and her clothes didn't look quite clean.

'Yeah?' she slurred. 'What you want?'

'Come out here. Someone for you to meet.' He nodded at Gail. 'She's here to help June until she gets back on her feet again.'

'She gonna take over?' A frown creased the girl's shiny forehead. 'Don't need *nobody* to 'take over.' *I can do it all by myself.*' She stared down at the cracked linoleum floor petulantly.

'Now don't you go pulling airs, my girl. This here's Gail Norris, *Miz* Norris to you, and she's here because *I* want her here, you understand?'

The girl nodded sullenly. 'Yessir, I unnerstand.'

Gail immediately had recognized the unmistakable signs of a mild form of Down's Syndrome. Her beloved brother, Erle, was afflicted with it, although his case was much more severe. He was quite literally a child trapped in a man's body. The other difference between them was that Erle Stanley Norris had been raised in a loving and caring home environment and as a result, he was always sweet-natured and cheerful and eager to please. This girl had probably been bounced from place to place without much care or understanding of her condition, and her moody resentment was a direct result.

Gail stepped forward and held out her hand toward Idy's grimy paw. 'I'm Gail, and it's perfectly all right for you to call me that. I'm here to help *you*, Idy, and I really need you to show me how to do that. It must be a very hard job, taking care of all the people here.' She gestured toward the still-grinning Jimmy. 'Especially with Mrs. Dunlap laid up. Mr.

Dunlap is just thinking of you, and thought you could really use the extra pair of hands. I'll be like . . . like *your* assistant, if that's all right with you.' She smiled warmly into the girl's dull eyes.

Idy hesitated, then reached out and touched Gail's hand with her own. 'OK, I guess that's all right then,' she muttered, then turned abruptly and stomped back into the main part of the house.

Frank eyed Gail with suspicion. 'Mustn't let her get away with throwing them tantrums of hers. Give her an inch and she'll take a mile. But that's on you. I'll let you two work it out.' He turned on his heel and started toward the door.

'Frank?' she said before his hand fastened on the knob. 'Where *is* Mrs. Dunlap? I'd really like to get acquainted and see if there's anything she needs.'

'Idy will show you,' he said.

Without further ado, he opened the door, stomped out and down the sway-backed steps and hopped into the jeep. With a roar of the motor and a cloud of red dust, Frank disappeared back down the hill from whence they had come.

4

Happy Families

'Here she is. Her name is June, but we all call her 'June Bug,'' Idy whispered, leading Gail into a sunny bedroom off the main living room of the house.

A double bed was angled into one corner, allowing tall French doors on either side to stand open to the wooden veranda, letting in a cool breeze and plenty of light. A stocky woman in her forties, heavily made up with lipstick, rouge and eye shadow, was propped up against several pillows and puffing greedily on a cigarette. Magazines and catalogs were scattered about the bed, and a table to one side held a lamp, tissues, an overflowing ashtray, and what looked like a half-full glass of beer.

'I got your 'care' lady here, June Bug,' Idy offered. 'She's Miz . . . her name is Gail. And she's here to help out . . . '

'C'mere,' June croaked in a throaty rasp, peering suspiciously as Gail made her way to the bed. 'Lemme get a look at you.'

'Hello, June,' Gail said, holding her hand out. 'How are you feeling? Is there anything I can get you . . . or do for you?'

'Idy,' June bellowed, ignoring Gail's proffered hand. 'I need me one of them pain pills. Now! This leg is hurting like a son-of-a-gun!'

'You just had one an hour ago,' Idy barked back. 'You know you ain't supposed to have more than two before Frank gets back. He's gonna be madder than — '

'Never you mind about Frank. He's not the one with the broken foot, is he? I need a pain pill now, and no mouthing back, y' hear?'

'Uh . . . June?' Gail spoke up. 'Why don't I take a look at the pills? There's usually instructions on the bottle. Maybe — '

'T'ain't none of *your* business, missy.' June slumped back against her pillow. 'My foot *hurts*! And I need my pills! Doctor gave them to *me*, and I guess I know if I need one or not.'

Gail turned quickly to Idy. 'Where are the pills, Idy? Would you get them and let me have a look at them? Then we can decide if it's time for Mrs. Dunlap to have another one.'

Idy, relieved to be released from the burden of decision, scurried away, and Gail turned firmly back to the cranky June Bug. 'Now, let's see if we can get you a little more comfortable here. Are you permitted to get out of bed? Maybe we could get you out to the living room chair, and you could watch some TV, take your mind off.'

'Get your hands off me,' snapped June. 'I don't need your help, and I *don't* want to go watch TV. I *told* Frank before I didn't want him bringing in no *damn* 'caregiver' to fuss and poke about. I *told* him. I thought we'd gotten that straight . . .' She took another vicious puff from her cigarette and reached over for the half-filled glass.

'Is that liquor?' Gail asked. 'If so, I really must advise you not to mix that with any sedative. It could be very dangerous for you.'

June gulped down most of the remaining liquid in one gasp. 'If all you can do is order me about in my own home, then I'm telling Frank to get rid of you, just like that other — ' She stopped short suddenly, as if she had been about to say something unintended.

'Other what?' Gail asked cautiously. 'Was there someone else here to help you recently? Someone who left?'

'No. I said no such thing. There's been nobody here. I just meant I don't take kindly to snotty people like you coming in and taking over. That's all. Didn't mean nothin' else.'

Idy returned with a small brown plastic vial which she handed without comment to Gail. Gail examined the label carefully, then nodded. 'This is an opiate, June, and you definitely can't be taking this if you're consuming alcohol at the same time. Why don't we wait until Frank comes back and talk it over with him? Perhaps you've misunderstood what the doctor told you.'

The mention of Frank getting involved seemed to take the wind out of June's sails, and she settled back on the bed without comment other than a brief, 'Well, it *still* hurts.' But she made no more demands for the medication as she picked up a magazine and began leafing idly through it, dismissing Gail with a brief nod of her head.

'Now,' Gail muttered to Idy, as the two retreated back out to the living area, 'where's Granny, and how long ago did you check on her? Has she had anything to eat?'

'Down here,' Idy responded almost eagerly, leading the way to a closed door opening out of the living room onto a long hallway. Opening the furthermost of two doors carefully, so as not to make any unnecessary noise, Idy tiptoed into another bedroom.

This room, however, was darkened, with curtains drawn tightly across the unopened windows, and the unmistakable odor of old urine and an unwashed body permeated the atmosphere. It took a moment for Gail to adjust her sight, but what she saw was troublesome. An emaciated form, wrapped tightly up in the bedclothes, was sleeping soundly in the midst of an ancient four-poster with a sagging mattress and scarred, dusty wooden posts and headboard. Her mouth was agape, and a slight hint of drool escaped from her lips. The stentorian rasp of a steady snore broke the silence of the stuffy room.

'How long has she been like this?' Gail asked, inwardly appalled at the obviously neglected flotsam of humanity before her. 'When was the last time she ate? Had water?'

'Oh, she don't like to eat none, so I don't *force* her. Frank says *never* force her to eat or anything. I guess she had some broth last night, but she spit most of it out. Don't think she really likes broth, but sometimes it's all I can get down her. Frank says broth is good for her . . . At least its *nourishing* — that's what Frank says.'

'He does, does he?' Gail was suddenly angry. 'Well, we're going to fix her something to eat now, Idy. Right now. Here, help me get her up. Do you know what she *does* like? Anything she might be happy to eat?'

Gail marched forward and patted the old woman gently on the shoulder, attempting to rouse her.

'Oh, she loves ice cream. She could eat a ton of it. But Frank says that's just dessert, and she has to eat something *nourishing* before she can get dessert.'

'Fine. You go out and fix her the biggest bowl of ice cream you can find. And chop up some fresh fruit over it, if you have any. Here — is there a clean nightgown I can put on her? I see she's got adult diapers on. Where do you keep them? Come on Idy, get a move on here. We need to get her up, cleaned up and *fed!*'

'Yes'm.' Idy, clearly into the swing of things now, bustled about laying out a fresh nightgown, diapers, wipes and a laundry bag for the used clothing.

'I'll go fix that ice cream now. But, ma'am . . . Gail? Would you please tell Frank it wasn't my idea? He's going to be real mad about this.'

'You leave Frank to me, Idy. I'll tell him it was all my idea. If he wants to get mad at anyone, he can get mad at me.'

A short while later, a much more alert and much less smelly Granny was seated in a comfy easy chair in the living room, eyes wide open and staring at the television tuned to some obscure soap opera.

'*Vas viltz du?*' she kept muttering, as she chugged down the huge bowl of ice cream and sliced strawberries fresh out of Pops's garden perched on the rickety little TV tray in front of her.

'What does that mean? Do you know? What she keeps saying,' Gail asked Idy, as they sat on either side of Granny, monitoring her carefully and wiping away the occasional dribble.

'I don't have a clue, but she says it all the time. Frank says he thinks it's German or something, and he thinks it might mean 'What's with you?' or something like that.' Idy took an idle swipe at a drip of melted ice cream making its way down Granny's chin.

'Hmmm. Sounds a bit like Yiddish to me,' said Gail, almost to herself. After the flurry of activity she found it somewhat relaxing to sit here chatting comfortably with a calmer Idy.

She had checked on June and found her snoozing away amongst her magazines and pillows. She had carefully removed the cigarettes, filthy ashtray and empty beer glass from the side table. She'd deal with that issue after Frank's return.

She started. Frank's return! 'Idy! What time is it? What on earth are we going to fix for supper? I forgot all about it while we were getting Granny settled.'

'Don't worry about it.' Idy waved her hand grandly. 'There's plenty of left-over fried chicken and potato salad from yesterday and Pops brought in some fresh stuff from the garden. Iced tea's already made; did it myself early this morning,' she added proudly.

'Good for you, Idy! I don't know what I'd do if you weren't here. Thank you so much for helping me. You're a good worker, and I'm glad we're doing this together.' She reached over and squeezed Idy's rough red hand in her own smooth one.

Idy smiled warmly at Gail. 'I'm glad

you're here, too, G . . . Gail. I hope *you* can stay a while longer,' she gulped, holding back a tear as a faint blush spread over her cheeks, making her look almost pretty. 'It sure is easier when there's two, isn't it?'

'Sure is, Idy. It's much easier with two.' Gail sat back and stared numbly at the flickering images on the screen in front of her. *'Vas viltz du? . . . Vas viltz du?'* Granny agreed, shoveling the last bit of ice cream in her gummy mouth.

And what's with you, Mr. Dunlap? Gail echoed in her mind. *What's with you, indeed?*

★ ★ ★

By the time Idy and Gail had laid out the cold supper, Frank's jeep came chugging up the hill. Pops and Jimmy were already seated at the big table in the end of the living room, eagerly tucking in their napkins, when the door opened and Gail was surprised to see a stranger enter the room.

'Oooh, it's Buck!' Idy whispered to her

excitedly. And Buck was a handsome fellow indeed, in his mid-thirties, tall, with dark hair and serious blue eyes. Idy scurried about setting an extra place as Frank came shuffling in behind and headed for the bathroom at the end of the annex to wash up.

'Hello,' the stranger said to Gail, who was pouring out iced tea into several large glasses. 'I'm Bill Brandon, but everyone around here calls me Buck. I take it you're Gail? Frank told me you're here to help out while June's laid up. Thought I'd drop by and make your acquaintance.'

'Hello,' she returned, somewhat flustered by the new arrival. 'Yes, Frank's hired me for a couple of months, just until June's back on her feet. As long as she doesn't overdo things until that ankle heals, I don't think there's anything to worry about.'

'Well, I'm sure they're glad for the help.' He gestured toward Idy, who was busy fixing trays for June and Granny. June had declined Gail's invitation to come out to the dinner table with the others, and Idy assured her that Frank

46

would 'blow his stack' if she dared bring Granny into the mix. After her afternoon treat of ice cream and TV, Granny seemed content to sit up in bed and leaf through some of June's magazines. Gail didn't think she was actually reading them, but she seemed to enjoy looking at the pictures.

'You're welcome to supper,' Gail added. 'It's just cold chicken, but I think we have plenty.'

'I guess I should explain who I am,' Buck continued. 'I've lived near here most of my life, except for a few years while I was attending college over on the coast. Got a degree in engineering, but I decided to come back here and see what I could do for the community. I manage the local mining office, which is an offshoot of the Bureau of Land Management. I keep track of all the old mining claims, and a few new ones.

'From time to time, as the price of gold fluctuates, people get interested all over again in mining opportunities. I try to make sure that everyone's rights are protected and make sense out of all the old maps of the area. Keeps me busy, and I think it serves a purpose for the people here.'

'That's great,' Gail said, nodding her head. 'I can see how challenging that might be, protecting people's property rights and all . . . ' She hesitated. Better not to go down that path too far. 'Of course I know nothing about all that sort of thing; but still, it sounds like fascinating work.'

'You should come into the office one day while you're here,' he said with a smile. 'I could show you the old historical maps. We could even take a ride out to one of the mines, if you'd be interested.'

'Well, I'll have to see how things go here, with June and all,' she said. 'But yes, if I have the time, I'd be very interested in the historical things.'

'Good. I'll talk to Frank about it and see if we can set something up then. Now I'd better go wash up.' And he headed down the hall where Frank had just emerged, hair wet, and stripped to his undershirt.

Pops and Jimmy were already tucking

into their plates of food as Frank and Buck took their places. Gail wondered if she and Idy would be consigned to the kitchen table, but Idy quickly sat down next to Buck and began talking to him earnestly in an undertone. He shook his head vehemently at one point, then seemed to ignore the girl.

Gail checked that everyone had what they needed in the way of utensils and took the remaining seat on the other side of the table.

Not much more conversation ensued, but the meal seemed to go well. Idy got up several times to check on Granny and to remove June's tray when she was finished.

'Ice cream, anyone?' Idy called out from the big freezer in the kitchen.

'Just bring the carton in here,' Frank ordered. 'No need in dirtying any extra dishes.'

So Idy brought in the big carton of ice cream from the freezer and spooned it out on top of the licked-clean plates. A big bag of store-bought cookies was passed around, and that made dessert.

Gail couldn't help but notice how Idy hung on every word Buck uttered and wondered just how long she had been pining after the handsome young man. Buck paid no attention to Idy for the rest of the meal, but made general conversation with Gail and Frank about the price of gold, the many old mines in the area, and the historical nature of the mining claims and property rights.

Once or twice Idy asked a question or made a comment but, in spite of Gail's efforts to draw her into the conversation, Buck made no effort to respond, choosing instead to ignore the girl, as did Frank.

After the food was put away and the dishes washed, Gail checked again on June and found her snoring away. A half-empty glass of beer sat on her table, along with the tiny vial of pain pills. When she asked Idy about it, the girl shrugged.

'Frank said it was OK. It's up to Frank. I can't go against him, not like I . . . ' Gail waited for Idy to complete the thought, but she shook her head and went off to settle Granny for the night.

Buck had left not long after supper,

walking back to his rental cabin behind the nearby mining office.

'Frank,' Gail said later, as she came out of June's room, 'I'm concerned about June drinking alcohol and taking those pain pills at the same time. I don't think that's safe.'

'Aw, it's all right,' he yawned, turning away from the TV. 'June will do her own thing, and I'm not inclined to interfere. She knows how much she can handle. And that foot *is* painful. Just let her be. All you need to worry about is keeping her fed and bathed and such. Just leave the rest of it alone.' He grabbed the remote and increased the sound on the sports program he was watching. Clearly, he was not going to discuss this particular subject any further with her.

Gail shrugged. 'Well, if there isn't anything else, I'm going up to bed.'

There was no answer. Pops and Jimmy had disappeared, presumably to their own hidey-holes. Idy was out in the kitchen, looking over the possibilities for tomorrow's meals. There wasn't anything else for her to do, so she took her silent leave and climbed the steep winding stair to the second floor rooms.

Thus ended her first day at Hangover Hill. It was going to be a long, hot summer.

5

Ashes to Ashes

At first Gail could not understand what she was hearing.

She had been tossing and turning most of the night, trying to find a comfortable spot on the lumpy old mattress. The tiny upstairs room was close and stuffy, and she had flung open the one window to the night air in an effort to get some relief from the evening breeze. Still she felt sticky and sweaty, and longed for morning when she could claim her time in the one shower.

She was considering the risk of creeping down the creaky old stairs when the noise took over. It was a loud clanging and banging, reminding her of a marching band with too many cymbals in the mix. Rising above the repeated *blat, blat, blare* of whatever was making the noise, she began hearing shouts and then . . . a scream!

'Fire! Fire! Everybody out!'

Gail wrapped her robe around her, scooted her feet into the slippers beneath the bed, grabbed the tote containing her purse and notebook off the bed post, and ran out the door, nearly taking down old Pops, who was shuffling dazedly out of his tiny room at the end of the hall.

'Here! Let me help you,' Gail shouted, grabbing him around his slender shoulders and guiding him to the top of the treacherous steps. There she paused.

'Where's Jimmy?' she asked urgently. 'Have you seen him?'

'He's not up here. He went back down to get some more ice cream. I didn't hear him come back, and I'm pretty sure he ain't up here.'

Gail nodded, keeping a firm hold on Pops. Slowly, they stumble-stepped their way down to the central corridor below. Gail saw immediately that their way was blocked toward the living area, spotting the black smoke inching under the first of the closed hallway doors.

'No,' she called to Pops, who was automatically heading towards the living room. 'I think the fire's coming from that direction. Is there another way out?' She peered anxiously behind them toward the front of the house, the part she had not yet explored.

'Yes there is,' Pops rasped, turning around and pointing behind them. 'That's the old front door. They never use it, since they park in back. I think it's locked, but the key might be in the lock.'

Carefully they retraced their steps to the vestibule beyond the stairway, and in spite of the smoke, Gail could barely make out the outline of the front door, just as Pops had described. She let go of him and fumbled around the handle until she found the keyhole. Yes! A skeleton key hung loosely from the lock. She turned it with a little effort, and the door squeaked open.

'Come on!' she called to Pops waiting behind her. 'Hurry! We've got to get out of here.' This thing's going to go up like tinder!'

She thought briefly of Granny, who would still be in her room just across from the staircase, then decided it would be best to get Pops to safety first, then come back and deal with the old woman, who might fight against leaving.

They stumbled out onto the wooden veranda which circled the entire house. Pops began coughing uncontrollably, and Gail stopped to alternatively pound him on the back then massage his thin upper chest. She had no idea if that would help, but it seemed to give him a bit of relief.

'Around here,' she instructed. 'The rescuers seem to be concentrated in the back.'

Just then, a familiar face peered around the corner of the house then started back in surprise at the sight of them.

'Buck!' she said with relief. 'I've got Pops here, but I think Granny may still be in her room. Can you help me?'

'No, she's already out. Frank got her out first, right after the fire started. Everybody else is safe and seems to be OK . . . except . . . ' He paused.

She could not read his face in the dim light, but something in the tone of his voice warned her that the next words would be unpleasant.

'Who? Is it June?' For some reason it had occurred to her that the demanding June was a thorn in Frank's side . . . one that he might not be too unhappy to lose.

'No. June's all right, too. Got right out of there through the French doors in her bedroom, even on that bad foot of hers. Didn't seem to bother her one little bit. We're still checking every possibility, but it looks like Idy's room, the one next to Granny's, was right where the fire started. I don't think she made it out.'

Tears started in Gail's eyes. She hardly knew the girl. But she had bonded with her over taking care of this motley crew, and Gail had to admit that Idy had been doing the best job she could, in spite of her handicaps. And Gail was reminded of her own special brother, Erle, who always tried so hard to do the best that he could. It wasn't fair. This shouldn't have happened, not to an innocent like Idy.

'Tell me, Buck,' Gail said, her voice suddenly cold and professional, 'do they know what caused the fire?' *Or who?* she added to herself, fighting back the tears. There was a mystery here, all right. And she would get to the bottom of it, or else.

'Well, they don't seem to have any idea yet of what caused it. Idy's room was the main one hit. There's some smoke and water damage throughout the rest of the house, of course, but there doesn't appear to be any real harm done to the main structure.'

By then they had reached the area where all the trucks and rescuers were gathered, and Gail's attention was directed to looking for and reassuring the bewildered survivors.

After determining which neighbors had spare rooms and could put up a few people for the night, including a retired nurse who volunteered to care for Granny, things gradually wound down while the remaining members of the volunteer fire department, with Frank in the lead, made their way through the smoke-filled house to check for stubborn embers.

As Gail made her way down toward the judge's house where she had been assigned a room, the pink fingers of a rosy dawn began to lengthen towards daylight.

★   ★   ★

Gail got through to Hugo on the second ring. She had snuck out early to use her cell phone, and had wandered down behind the judge's garden to a small frog pond at the bottom of the hill.

'Sorry,' came the terse reply. 'I was just bringing Connie up to date.'

'That's all right,' she said. 'I figured as much.'

'Boss man ain't happy,' he added.

She ignored the remark. 'Have you found out anything at all?'

'Pretty much what you figured. It was arson all right. They found accelerant right inside Idy's bedroom door. That couldn't have been an accident. There was no way she could have gotten out past it. Another thing: the windows in her room had been blocked. She wouldn't have been able to open them from the inside.

'One other small detail. There was a bump or bruise on the back of her head, severe enough, they figure, to have knocked her out cold. They've more or less surmised that she fell and hit it trying to get out of the room, but . . . '

Anger surged through Gail, causing the bile to rise in her throat, and angry tears splashed from her eyes. 'So Idy *was* the target.' She thought a minute.

'Darn. Frank's insisting on having the funeral day after tomorrow and she'll be buried in the cemetery here immediately after. You know what that means.'

'Yeah. If there *is* to be any further investigation, we may have to have her exhumed. I don't think we have enough evidence right now to — '

'What about this judge here? Have you dug up anything on him? Where does he stand in all this?'

'Judge Cooley? He seems to be all right. He's a direct descendant of the first Cooley who founded the town and I guess he's been judge here forever. I think it's almost a hereditary post by now. There was one thing, though.'

'Don't tell me the judge has a skeleton in the closet.'

'Well, he was married briefly, to a much younger woman . . . sort of a gadabout from San Francisco. With a bit of a checkered past, from what the local gossip says.

'Anyway, a few years back she got into some kind of altercation in the tavern. Not sure what it was about — no one seems to remember. After she went back home, she went into their bathroom, plunked herself down on the commode, stuck the business end of a shotgun in her mouth and pulled the trigger with her big toe — '

'Wow! Well that's quite a revelation. Any idea why she did it? And were they absolutely sure it was self-inflicted?'

'Doesn't seem to be any doubt about the latter; all the forensics pointed to a self-inflicted wound and there didn't seem to be anyone else around at the time. The judge was conveniently out of town. It appeared she had planned to do it while he was gone so she wouldn't be interrupted. As for motive . . . there was some talk that she had had a recent cancer diagnosis. For some, that would be motive enough, I suppose.'

'Hmm. I suppose he could have hired

someone to do it. Any other suspicious characters or events to report?' Gail asked.

'I have a few ideas of course, but nothing concrete enough to make any accusations as yet.'

Gail hesitated. 'Please try to explain to Connie that I'm right in the middle of things here. I definitely believe there *is* something more sinister going on, but I can't quite put my finger on it yet. Ask him to give us just a few more days and maybe we can wrap this up.

'This fire was a huge mistake on someone's part. I can't help but feel the two things are connected — Sonia's disappearance and now Idy's death. Murder I'd call it. What do you think?'

'I think you're probably right about that. I'll start digging into Idy's back-ground a bit, see if something crawls out. And I'll tell Connie I think you're all right for the moment. Just don't get too nosy. Someone's getting real antsy here. And I don't like it. Not one little bit. If you have any problem at all, call me right away. Keep that phone on you at all times, just in case.'

'Will do. And, Hugo . . . thank you for being such a great back-up. I sure was relieved you were on that bus with me. Makes me feel a whole lot safer to know you're here looking out for me.'

As she disconnected the call, something kept nagging at the back of her brain. Something that she had heard that didn't seem quite right, but she couldn't put her finger on it.

She headed back to the judge's house lost in thought. As she entered the back door into the kitchen, the aroma of frying bacon and brewing coffee reminded her she hadn't eaten yet.

A pleasant voice greeted her from the stove. 'Back from your walk? Sit down over here and have a cup of coffee while I finish up breakfast. I like company when I cook. Did you sleep all right?'

The speaker was a tall man, six foot five at least, with a slender, somewhat gangly build. His gaunt, Lincolnesque facial features were softened by a welcoming smile and friendly brown eyes beneath a shock of silver-gray hair.

'Good morning, Judge. I certainly slept

well. Your guest room is very comfortable, and I thank you so much for offering it to me last night . . . after such a terrible experience.'

'I'm glad you slept all right. You're welcome to stay as long as you like. Smoke can be terribly irritating. I feel very sorry for the young woman involved. Death is such a final thing . . . ' He suddenly turned his attention back to the stove.

'Judge? I'm wondering if there will be any kind of investigation of the . . . event, by the local authorities, I mean?'

'Local authorities? Well, there aren't any to speak of. I guess I'm the most authority in these parts, and I don't really have jurisdiction over something like this. As you must have realized last night, we only have a volunteer fire department, made up entirely of local citizens — basically whoever's available when something like this happens. Fire is dreaded in this area, with all the dry timber about, and limited access. So when fire strikes, in whatever manner, every capable man turns out in a hurry to prevent the scourge from spreading. Folk around here are pretty good about pitching in and lending a hand when it's necessary. Otherwise, they prefer to keep to themselves.

'So there really isn't any local entity to get involved. Oh, I suppose we could call in the State Forestry, but they're spread thin this time of year, with all the fire hazards up and down this drought-ridden state.'

Gail frowned. 'What about the police or sheriff?'

The judge shook his head. 'I doubt it. The closest substation is up the road a piece in Duneville — or back down all the way to Nevada City, or even Grass Valley, which is even further. Nope, I doubt if we're going to get much help there. People around here mostly police themselves. Everybody knows everybody. Somebody gets out of line, it'll be taken care of — one way or t'other — in time.'

He busied himself shoveling fried eggs and bacon onto two china plates, added a stack of buttered toast, and filled up Gail's cup before taking his seat at the table beside her.

'But if it's foul play?' Gail persisted. 'I'm sorry sir, but it angers me a bit to think someone might have caused this, for whatever reason, and that poor girl died because of it.' She took a sip of the blistering hot coffee and reached for a slice of toast.

'Believe me, I understand what you're saying,' the judge said, dipping the corner of his toast into a pool of golden egg yolk. 'But I've learned the hard way — you can't fight city hall . . . and in the case of Cooleyville, you can't change reality.'

* * *

There was a fair turn-out for Idy's funeral. The grange hall was half-full of mostly middle-aged couples who had come to pay their respects to the young girl.

Gail sat near the back, her emotions playing back and forth between anger and sorrow. It became obvious that Idy was not that well-known in the town, and the bespectacled young Protestant preacher they had brought in to speak for her struggled to find words to comfort the congregation. As he mumbled something about her 'kindness towards others' and 'finding her place in heaven,' Gail felt like standing up and screaming in protest. But she sat silently, head bowed through the interminable service, then filed out with the others into the bright sunlight of another hot day.

Only a few of the mourners followed the casket across the street and up the hill to the cemetery where, after a few brief words, poor Idy was laid to rest. Gail had picked a few stray flowers earlier that morning where they grew at random at the edge of Pop's garden. She paused a moment in reflection, then laid them gently to one side of the gaping hole which held all that remained of the troubled young girl.

By the time she turned away most of the others had begun making their way back to the iron double gates near the street. One person remained behind, watching her as she waded through the tall grass. As she neared him, he held out his hand.

'Careful there, Gail. Wouldn't want you to take a fall,' Buck said with concern.

'I'm fine,' she said, avoiding his offer of assistance. 'But thanks anyway. Are you coming back up to the house for something to eat?'

Several of the local women had brought in casseroles and salads 'to tide the family over' in a gesture of goodwill. She sighed. It would be a long afternoon.

'No, I think I'll pass on it. I'll try to get by a little later on, once things have settled down a bit. I think you probably have enough to worry about right now, without me looking for a handout.'

'Well, all right. I guess I'll see you later on then.'

Frank, Pops and Jimmy were waiting for her by the gate. 'Come on, Gail,' Frank called. 'We need to get back to the house now, before anyone else shows up.'

She picked up her pace to catch up, and immediately put Buck Brandon out of her mind. Time enough to deal with him later in the week. Right now it seemed like a good idea to make sure she was still welcome on Hangover Hill.

She had wanted to pay for the funeral, and it took all of her willpower to refrain from offering; even when later that evening, after all the visitors had left, Frank began grumbling to her about what all this was going to cost him. The fire damage alone, he said, was going to take several thousand dollars to repair, even with him and a few of his buddies doing all the work. Paying for the funeral and burial costs as well was going to 'damn near break' him, he claimed.

Gail gritted her teeth through his recitation. When he was finished with the tirade, she smiled sweetly at him. 'Under the circumstances I'd be glad to offer to stay on for a while longer without you paying me. I can get by on just the room and board for a few weeks. I'll consider it to be like my summer vacation.'

'Would you do that? Really?' His relief was palpable. 'I just relied on Idy so much to keep things running smoothly here while I had to be out working. I'd sure be grateful, Gail, if you'd be willing to do that ... under the circumstances ... ' he added, letting the words fall off into silence.

'All right then,' she said lightly. 'Just so long as you don't expect gourmet cooking. I'll get the food on the table when you need it, and continue looking after June and Granny. But I expect I'll need to get back home by the end of next month. I can't afford to do it any longer than that.'

'That'll be fine. I might be able to find another one of the young girls around here looking for something to do by then. Maybe you can talk to a few of them for me? Sort them out?'

Other young girls!

'Sure, Frank. I'd be glad to do that.' She got up from the kitchen table and went to the sink to begin washing the dishes. She was still shaking with anger inside, but outwardly she managed to act normally.

As she peered out through the dirt-encrusted window over the sink, she thought she saw a figure moving furtively through the underbrush on the other side of the garden. She wondered if someone had been eavesdropping through the open window as she and Frank had talked.

She watched a minute, then shook her head. It was probably an animal of some kind. There were plenty of them around. She had seen possums, tons of stray cats, and even a beautiful young fox had run through the yard on one occasion as she watched breathlessly. Could have been anything. A rat, perhaps.

Even a two-legged one . . .

6

Message from Beyond

Frank's 'strays,' as Gail had begun to think of them, were all moved back in within a few days once the house had aired out thoroughly, and the routine quickly got back to normal, at least the Hangover Hill normal.

Several mornings after Idy had been laid to rest in the big grassy cemetery below the house, Buck came into the kitchen and waited while Frank finished his morning ablutions in the one big bathroom at the end of the hall. When Frank emerged, shaking his rough hairy head like some shaggy water buffalo, Buck hailed him over a steaming cup of coffee.

'*Hola*, Frank. How's it going?' He sounded cheerful and upbeat, almost as if the tragedy of a few nights before had never occurred.

'Oh, I'm OK, I guess.' Frank yawned

and stretched, pouring himself a steaming cup and helping himself to the platter of bacon and eggs Gail had prepared.

'Well, I've got some news for you. You, too,' he added, beaming at Gail.

She looked back at him warily. She was trying to keep a real low profile now, and deliberately had not taken part any further in the family discussions about the fire or Idy's death.

'The community has decided to hold a benefit to raise money to help pay for repairs to the house — and maybe something towards Idy's final expenses as well. We're putting on a square dance and box supper social at the grange hall Saturday night. There'll be a small fee for entrance, the local ladies will bring the food and set it up buffet-style, and old Dad Jones and his boys will provide the music and caller. I think it will be a real success, and might even make enough to buy the lumber you need to fix that room up.' He nodded towards the damaged part of the house where Idy's room lay in ruins.

Gail stared at him. He seemed happy

and relaxed, almost as if nothing had happened. She shrugged. 'All right with me,' she said. 'If everyone else is up for it, I'll be glad to help if I can.'

'Great!' Buck said, grinning at her. 'I just thought we could use a little brightening up around here. What say, Frank? Are you on board?'

'Sure.' Frank busied himself with his coffee and toast. 'Sure, that's all right. I could use a little financial assistance right about now. More the merrier, I say.'

★   ★   ★

Later that afternoon, the screen door suddenly swung open and a deep woman's voice called out, 'Frank? Where the hell are you?'

Gail had been straightening up the pillows around June's bed and turned to answer, but June grabbed her wrist and shook her head violently. 'Don't you dare let her in here . . . Get rid of her. I won't have her in here.' Her urgent whisper beat counterpoint to the calls from the other room.

74

'All right,' Gail reassured her. 'I'll just go see what she wants.'

By the time Gail reached the living room, a large unkempt woman had clomped in and flung herself down on the easy chair in front of the TV.

'Sure is a lot cooler in here than over at my place. All that heat rises, ya know. You don't know how good you have it.' She squinted up at Gail. 'Who the hell are you? You that new girl Frank hired? Just in time, I'd say, now that worthless Idy's kicking up the dandelions.'

Gail caught herself just in time from responding angrily to the crude mention of Idy. 'Yes, I'm Gail Norris. I'm staying on for just a couple more weeks . . . just until June's back on her feet. And you are — ?'

'Oh hell. Sorry I didn't introduce myself. I'm Frank's cousin, Winnie. I live in that apartment over the garage over there.' She pointed vaguely in the direction of an ancient two-story wooden structure leaning precariously near the front of the parking area.

'You *live* there?' Gail tried to keep the

disbelief out of her voice but failed miserably.

'Yeah. Frank's folks — my aunt Clarissa and uncle Joe — used to live there. When my uncle died, Frank took Clarissa — Granny, they all call her now — in here. He let me move into the apartment after that. I don't pay no rent. He'd never get anyone to pay rent there anyhow. But it's a roof over my head. I fell on some hard times, after my husband was killed . . . '

'Your husband was *killed?*' For such a small town, the mortality rate certainly seemed high.

'In the mine. Roof collapsed and the whole thing caved in on him. Funny thing is, I have no idea why in God's name he was in there in the first place. Well, he had been a bit down in the dumps since Mattie, our daughter, disappeared. I kept tellin' him, 'She's just gone off to see the world,' but he wasn't havin' any of it. Got to wanderin' around out in the sticks, pokin' his nose into places he shouldn't, I warrant. Well, no help for it, now.' She shrugged and mopped a sweaty brow with a crumpled up tissue.

'Well, I'm sorry for your loss,' Gail murmured absently. 'Frank's not here right now, and June's taking a nap. Can I deliver a message to him for you when he gets in?'

'Nope. Just checkin' in to let him know I'll come over and Granny-sit while you all go to the party on Saturday. I reckon June can pretty much fend for herself, but Granny has a tendency to wander off if nobody's keepin' an eye on her.'

'Oh, all right, I'll tell him.' Gail wondered if Winnie intended to stay put right there in the easy chair, but after a minute or two, she struggled to her feet again and headed toward the door.

'Okey-doke, Miz Gail. See ya Saturday night. Nice to meetcha.'

'Nice to meet you too,' Gail said, as the screen slammed in her face. 'Very nice indeed.'

★ ★ ★

Saturday night arrived soon enough, and as Gail made her way upstairs to change for the party, she started suddenly when she realized Jimmy was waiting for her on the dim landing, the same vacant grin plastered across his face. 'Oh! You startled me!' she couldn't help saying, more in admonition than real fright. 'I might have fallen.'

'Sorry. Didn't mean to scare you,' he said, nodding vigorously. 'I got something to show you. I've been watching you, and I think you can handle this.'

'Er, I'm sorry Jimmy, but I've got to get ready for the party tonight. Could we do this some other time?' Gail had no intention of letting herself get cornered alone with Jimmy.

'It'll just take a minute, ma'am,' he said politely. 'It's really important. I have a message for you . . . from . . . *beyond*.'

'Beyond? What do you mean? You're not talking about the supernatural, are you, Jimmy?' She felt a slight shiver creep over her, in spite of the stifling heat. 'I don't really believe in that sort of thing.'

'Oh, that's all right. You don't *have* to believe. But I could give you the message anyway. That is, White Feather could.

He's my Indian spirit guide. He gives me messages all the time. And this one is really important. It's about that girl — '

'What girl, Jimmy? Do you mean Idy? What message about what girl?' Gail felt her heart begin to pound and her lungs constrict. Was the answer as simple as this? Something the old man had seen and kept hidden, but now was willing to divulge to her?

'Tell me, Jimmy. I *do* want to know.'

'If you want to know,' he said cagily, 'you'll have to come in here and look at my picture.'

'What picture? Come on, Jimmy, quit talking in riddles. I don't have the time for it.' Gail was suddenly quite calm, and spoke to him clearly and persuasively.

'Here. Come see . . . ' Jimmy backed into his tiny garret filled with an old army cot and a heavy footlocker in pride of place under the one grimy window. The locker was standing open and a few items had been retrieved and lay scattered across a tattered quilt.

Jimmy carefully picked up a battered 5×7 picture frame containing what looked like a primitive pastel drawing. He wiped it off with his sleeve, then turned to Gail. '*This* is what I wanted you to see,' he said, proudly holding the picture out to her.

She took it carefully in both hands and bent it toward the limited light from the window. The crude depiction was that of an Indian chief in full regalia, seated on a stool and staring straight ahead. One white eagle's feather stood up from the headdress, pointing skyward. One hand was placed in his lap and the other, index finger outstretched, seemed to beckon the viewer to join him.

'What a lovely old drawing,' she said, handing it back to Jimmy. 'Is it a likeness of a real person?'

'Oh, yes!' Jimmy exclaimed. 'He was real all right. Still is. I mean, he died many, many years ago, but he still comes back to me. He warns me about things. And tells me things maybe I shouldn't know . . . ' His voice trailed off uncertainly.

'What things, Jimmy? Does he warn you about things that are going to happen

— or maybe he tells you the truth about things that have already taken place? What do you think?'

'Both, maybe, but mostly he tells me about things I already knew but forgot. Little things — like something someone said one time and everyone else forgot.' He fidgeted a bit, as if making his mind up about something. 'I told Idy about it — about the *secret* — the one White Feather reminded me about. She didn't believe me at first, until I showed her this picture. Then she started to believe. That's why I wanted *you* to see it. You're a smart lady. You'll figure it out. Idy wasn't smart enough to do anything. That's why . . . that's why she had to *die*!'

Gail's blood froze in her veins. She did not for a moment believe in the old man's spirit guide, or that he was getting messages from the dead, but she did believe that people sometimes were capable of remembering little things — incidents that seemed unimportant at the time — then putting it all together later. If Jimmy wanted to think White Feather was telling him what he already knew, then so be it. But he might very well have seen or heard something he wasn't supposed to. Sitting in his little corner, smiling absently to himself, he might be almost invisible to someone caught up in some kind of scheme.

'Jimmy, you mentioned something about a girl, and I don't think you meant Idy. Who was she, Jimmy? What other girl were you talking about? *What do you know?*'

But Jimmy just smiled blankly, carefully wrapped up the glass-fronted picture and tucked it away in the old footlocker. 'No, ma'am. You got me wrong. I'm all confused again now. I don't know anything at all. Not one thing.' He stood and pointed at the door, much as the old Indian chief had pointed into space.

'Time to go now, missy. Time to get ready for your party.'

★   ★   ★

The large gravel parking lot at the grange hall was full when Frank, Gail and Buck arrived to join the festivities. Winnie, true

82

to her word, had arrived just as they were ready to leave the house. June had begged Frank to bring her down in the jeep, so she could 'just get out of the house a bit,' but he declined, saying she'd 'just be in the way.' She took another pill, had him fill her beer glass to the top, and sullenly settled down again with her movie magazines.

Gail had fed Granny early and tucked her into her bed. There was still a faint hint of smoke in the air, but it hadn't seemed to harm the old lady yet, to Gail's relief.

Winnie promised to check in on the two women every hour or so, and Gail had left in hopes that all would be well while they were at the party. 'Remember,' she cautioned Winnie and gesturing to her cell phone, 'I'll only be a few minutes away at the most, so if you need me for anything at all just give me a call. I'll come right back.'

'Will do, kiddo,' Winnie answered from the same easy chair she had commandeered earlier. 'Don't bother your pretty little head about it.'

Pops had elected an early bed time, and Jimmy, like June, had been banned from attending by Frank. 'Old coot gets a bit testy if he drinks too much,' he muttered. 'I don't want to have to bail him out of some situation.'

The first thing Gail noticed as they entered the hall was a group of young women going about the small wooden dance floor with buckets, and flinging what looked like sand on the floor. 'What are they doing?' she asked Buck. Frank had deserted them almost immediately to seek out his friends at the bar.

'Them?' He gestured at the women shuffling slowly around the floor, scattering the sand as they went. She nodded. 'They're 'sanding' the dance floor. Makes it less slippery for the dancers' boots.'

Gail was still pondering the sand shufflers when her attention was drawn toward the bar. Nearly every man gathered there was wearing some version of a red shirt. Most of the more boisterous among them were sporting bright red T-shirts adorned with colorful badges and buttons pinned to them, and clanking tin cups tied with rope to their belt loops. Even Judge Cooley, who was standing slightly apart with a group of older, more sedate couples, had on a neatly pressed red dress shirt tucked into his dress slacks, and with a small insignia of sorts pinned to the lapel. He looked up as they passed and nodded to her pleasantly.

'What on earth?' she exclaimed, looking about in amazement. 'Why are all those men wearing red shirts?' She suddenly remembered that Frank also was wearing a red T-shirt with paraphernalia pinned to it. She hadn't thought much of it when they left the house, thinking it might have something to do with the proposed square-dancing entertainment.

But now she saw that he fitted right in with the rest of the noisy bunch of men, laughing and joshing and raising their tin cups filled with foaming beer to each other in endless toasts. No wonder the place was called Hangover Hill!

'Clampers,' replied Buck. He was one of the few men in the hall who was not wearing red. '*E Clampus Vitus*. Haven't you heard of them?'

'Clampers? No, I haven't. *E Clampus Vitus?* What in the world does *that* mean?'

'The 'Latin' means nothing. It's all made up. They're a fraternal organization of sorts. Started up, they claim, back in the gold rush days, before the Civil War. Groups of miners congregated and made up this club for themselves, making fun of what they considered to be the more 'uppity' groups like the Masons and such. It nearly disappeared during the 1860s, but following the war they reorganized; and from time to time, like in the 1930s and again in the 1950s, there have been efforts to revitalize and strengthen the various lodges, mostly throughout the western United States. I've got a whole bunch of material on it down at the mining office, if you're interested.'

'But what do they *do?* Do they have any purpose, other than to party and drink?' She glanced at the rowdy group, now divided between the drinks area and stomping in their boots about the sanded dance floor to Dad Jones's squealing bluegrass music.

'Oh sure. Their main purpose from the day they were founded until now, other than the partying and drinking, is to look after their mining buddies. In the early days they would make sure the older prospectors always had food and shelter, and would even trek miles into the wilderness just so the old cusses wouldn't have to spend Christmas alone out on their 'diggins.' But the really wonderful thing they do is to look after what they call the 'widders and orphans.'' They make sure that any miner's family does not want for anything in time of need. And that truly is a plus.

'So many of the men who have worked in the mines, particularly in the earlier days, have nothing to show for it, and have left no provision for emergencies. If they died suddenly, their families were left destitute, often starving and without a roof over their heads. The Clampers always have pitched in to make sure that one of their own will not suffer like that.'

'That is a wonderful thing,' Gail said

thoughtfully. 'So that's what this party is all about. The Clampers are taking care of Frank right now.'

Just as he is taking care of all his 'strays' — *Pops, Jimmy and Winnie . . . and Granny, even though she is his own mother.* It gave her pause for a moment.

Maybe Frank *wasn't* the villain in this tale. But how was she to know the truth, if there was no one willing to tell her?

★ ★ ★

By the time Buck and Gail had assisted the well-oiled Frank back up Hangover Hill, it was well past midnight and the full moon had risen like a giant yellow plate, lighting their way so sufficiently that they scarcely needed the flashlight Buck had produced.

'I'm all right,' Frank kept insisting, although he was listing very badly to one side. 'Just need a little coffee . . . get me goin' again . . . '

'I think you need a little sleep first,' Buck muttered, hoisting him up the steps and into the kitchen.

Gail took a quick look at her charges, noting they all seemed to be sleeping soundly, including Winnie, propped with her feet up in the easy chair. She woke with a start when they clomped into the room with Frank, and roused herself enough to declare, 'Well, Frank, I see you couldn't stay out of the punch bowl again, could ya?' She yawned and moved her bulk out of the seat and helped Buck push Frank down into it.

He landed with a solid *whoomph*, laid his head back at an alarming angle and immediately began snoring.

'Probably best just to leave him there,' commented Winnie. 'He'll sleep like a log until morning. Need anything else?' she asked Gail.

'No, I can manage. Thanks for helping out tonight. I really appreciated it.'

'That's all right. Gives me something to do. Just let me know any time you need a break. I'll be glad to come over and get out of that heat.' Winnie busied herself gathering the few things she'd brought with her and turned to head out the door.

'Just a minute, Winnie.' Both Gail and Winnie were startled by Buck's voice calling the older woman back.

'What's up, Buck? Did I forget something?'

'Nope. I just thought maybe I would take you up on your offer, on Gail's behalf. Would you mind coming over and sitting with June and Granny tomorrow afternoon for a couple of hours? I promised I'd show Gail around the mining office. Since her time here is going to be limited now, I don't want her to get away without seeing what it is I actually do for a living.' He gave a self-deprecating little laugh.

'Oh, I don't know if that's such a good idea . . . ' Gail began, but was quickly interrupted by Winnie.

'Sure, I'd love to come over and sit a spell with the invalids. No problem at all.' She turned again and headed down the steps. 'See you tomorrow,' she called out over her shoulder. 'I'll be over a little after noon.'

'So, *that's* taken care of,' Buck said, almost to himself, as if he was checking off a 'To Do' list. 'Are you all right now?' he asked Gail. 'If you've got everything under control, I'll go on home. Got a few things I need to do before I turn in. Homework, you know.' He grinned at her from the moonlit doorway, then turned away and hopped nimbly down the steps.

Gail checked June and Granny one more time, gave a cursory glance to the sprawled-out Frank snoring loudly in the easy chair, then headed up the stairs to her room. She would need to get her sleep tonight, if she was going to take Buck's tour with any hope of staying awake through it all.

She glanced out her window at the big yellow moon once again, before climbing in to bed to dream of red-shirted men dancing in the sand.

7

The Old Clarissa

True to her word, Winnie showed up the next afternoon and clumped her way into the living room and plunked down in the easy chair. She picked up a *TV Guide* and began perusing it, searching for her favorite soaps. Gail took once last peek at June and Granny, both happily paging through the seemingly endless supply of magazines from June's stash, then waved at Winnie and stepped out onto the porch.

It was a beautiful day, with a clear blue sky; and it was a shade cooler, with a light breeze blowing through the pines and grasses just down the hill. Gail felt almost guilty, as if she was playing hooky from school. Still, there must be some clue she and Hugo had missed. If she could learn anything at all from Buck's documents at the mining office, it was worth the try.

She headed out the east side of the property, where the road curved, and in short order was climbing the cement steps to the mining office located just opposite the Dunlap property and next to a small but modern public school, silent now during summer vacation.

A tiny bell tinged as she opened the door, and a young woman looked up and smiled at her from the reception desk. 'Hi. I'm Marcy. You must be Gail . . . Buck's expecting you. Just go down that hall. His office is the first door on the right.'

'Thank you,' she said, looking about the outer office with interest. There were several large framed maps of various vintages hung on the wall, and off to one side a small table and chairs sat next to a low display case filled with what looked to be old record books.

As she made her way down the hall a door opened and Buck stepped out, a welcoming grin on his face.

'You made it! Great! Come on in, but don't mind the mess . . . '

He ushered her in to a small cramped

office furnished with a metal desk painted institutional gray, several straight-backed chairs and a large filing cabinet. Cardboard boxes crammed with papers sat on the floor around the perimeter of the room, and more stacks of documents were piled on the desk.

'That's all right. It must be a challenge, looking after all this material.' She perched a bit uncomfortably on the edge of one of the chairs. 'But tell me, Buck — what is it actually that you do here at the mining office?'

'Well, I can give you the long story, but the gist of it is that during the gold-rush era, primarily during 1849 and 1850, there were thousands of claims established throughout this area of California. Some of them were viable and the owners went on to realize earnings from them — in some cases, fortunes even.

'But the vast majority of them petered out. The original claimants either abandoned them outright, or in the worst-case scenario, died with their boots on, so to speak. At some point in time, the Bureau of Land Management took on the task of finding all of these old mine sites, establishing whether or not they were the property of existing claim holders, and making sure that all AMLs — abandoned mine lands, that is — were checked for safety hazards.

'Many of the mines that were built in the early days did not conform to the safety and environmental requirements we have today. So what the bureau does, with the assistance of engineers like me, is hunt up all these old claims and sites and go over them with a fine-toothed comb, just to be sure there are no safety issues lying in wait for unsuspecting hikers and hunters — or prospective miners. It's a difficult task, but a worthy one I think.'

He paused and pointed at the boxes and piles of paper massed around his desk. 'There's my work of a lifetime. I've spent the last ten years searching out and mapping all these sites — and I still have a ton of them left to do.'

'Wow! Sounds like a daunting task indeed.' Gail looked about, trying to imagine what it must be like to deal with such an unending pile of work. 'I'm surprised you have time for anything else in such a busy schedule.'

'Oh, it's not so bad. When I get tired of working in here, I just go out and look at one of the mines. I often check them several times a year, just to be sure nothing's changed — no flooding, erosion and the like. Can't be too safe, you know.'

He paused, then looked up as if he'd just had a thought. 'Say, how would you like to go out and visit one of the mines with me this afternoon? It's a beautiful day, and we could stop at a place out on the state highway on the way back and have something to eat. There's a little café down there that makes great burgers.'

Gail thought a moment. 'How long would it take? I shouldn't leave Winnie too long . . . '

'Not long — an hour or two at the most. I suspect Frank's going to be home early this afternoon. He must have a giant hangover after that party last night.' He grinned. 'Come on. You've been working very hard since . . . ' He left unsaid the obvious: since Idy's death.

'Well, all right. If you're sure it won't

take any longer than that. Might be fun.'

'Great. Go on out and wait for me in the reception office. I need to grab a few things and we can be on our way.'

Gail went into the outer room and began looking at the various maps on the wall. It did seem like interesting work, and Buck certainly seemed to be devoted to his job.

She stopped when something caught her eye and turned to Marcy. 'Excuse me. This diagram here is labelled 'The Clarissa Mine.' Can you tell me if it was named for Clarissa Dunlap, Frank's mother?'

'Oh yes, ma'am. That's the mine her husband, Joe, took over. He renamed it for her. They were a charming old couple, always the first ones on the dance floor at any of the gatherings. Sad how that has turned out for her, isn't it?' She smiled at Gail, then turned back to the work on her desk.

Gail studied the map with great interest for several minutes. She had turned to another map and was just starting to ask another question when Buck came in carrying a large canvas back pack. 'Let's go,' he said. 'Don't want to keep you out too late.'

The last thing Gail remembered, as they walked out the door and clambered into Buck's waiting SUV, was the sub-title under 'The Clarissa Mine' which read: 'The Smallest Mine in the Cooleyville Area.'

★ ★ ★

As they rounded the turn and headed down the hill toward the main highway, Buck turned and smiled at her. 'I'm glad we can do this today. I didn't want you to get away before I . . . ' He paused to shift down on the steep slope as they passed the grange. 'Before I . . . '

'Oh, look,' Gail said, interrupting his train of thought. 'There's Frank's jeep parked in front of the Gold Digger. I wonder what he's doing back in town? He said he had to be at work out on the highway this morning.'

Buck laughed. 'And you believed that old reprobate? Frank often spends half the day or more in there. Likely as not he has some girl on the string — but the real reason is, he loves his booze. Problem is, he often forgets where he's supposed to be and when. Why, he even — '

'What? Did he forget to do something important . . . some appointment or place he needed to be?' Gail suddenly had a thought. *What if Frank had been holed up in the tavern the afternoon Sonia's bus came in?*

'Oh, I just meant he's a bit lax, that's all.' Buck paused, as if he was giving the matter some thought. 'Truth is, old June has a contract with the U.S. Postal Service to carry the mail up to Pine Cone two or three times a week.'

'Pine Cone? Where's that?'

'Actually I was raised there. It's a tiny community about 7 or 8 miles back off of the main highway . . . too far from here for people to walk in and get their mail daily. June would take the jeep and carry the mail and bring back whatever folks there had going out. Made a nice little job for her, and helped pay some of the food bills. When she hurt her foot she couldn't drive and Frank had to take over for her.

'He's supposed to make the run twice a week while she's out of commission. Trouble is, Frank has a tendency to forget such things, especially when he's been in the tavern for a while. What I was about to say was that he even has been forgetting to carry the mail on occasion. That's all.'

Gail was silent a moment, thinking hard. But if Frank forgot to do something so routine as to carry the mail to Pine Cone twice a week, what else might he forget to do? Had he forgotten to meet Sonia's bus? But if she had actually been on that particular bus, what had happened to her after she'd got off?

Buck glanced over at her as they turned onto Highway 80 and headed east. 'Penny for your thoughts, Gail. You look like you've seen a ghost or something.'

Gail smiled at him and shook her head. But she said nothing further about Frank and his lapses. Still, she couldn't help but wonder, *Did someone else pick Sonia up from the bus stop? And if so, who could it have been?*

The beautiful mountain scenery whizzed by her as Buck picked up speed on the highway. There wasn't much traffic, only a few logging trucks rumbling to and from the various lumber mills dotted about the area. Gold had once been the cash crop here, but now, for the time, it was lumber. Unless the environmentalists had their way. The same restrictions on harvesting the mighty centuries-old trees would most likely have the same effect on the industry as the restrictions on mining activities. When the use of huge hydraulic guns to tear down the mountainsides to get at the valuable ore deposits was banned, the costs of mining became prohibitive. Determined and dedicated prospectors went back to digging into the lodes by hand, using shovels and pickaxes, but the glory days were gone.

It was a trade-off, Gail supposed. The economy versus the environment. It was a battle that had not yet been won, by either side.

She sat back in the car seat and enjoyed the sights and the cool breeze flowing through her open window. The scent of pine permeated the air. This was truly a paradise of sorts.

But what sort of demented serpent was working its evil on the people living here? Would she be able to unmask him before he inflicted any more harm?

8

Oblivion

The blazing sun thundered over the yardarm of the sinking ship . . . What?

Gail shook her head. Her neck ached from where she had propped herself against the hard rock surface. She must have been dreaming — some line from an old novel or poem. She realized with a start that she had been unconscious for . . . how long? A few minutes? An hour? Longer?

Painfully, she stretched her legs, one by one, then tentatively pulled herself upright, still clinging to the rough wall. The last thing she remembered clearly, after arriving at the secluded mine site on a bumpy dirt road — trail, really — several miles off the main highway, was how abandoned the place seemed.

There was no one else there, although she didn't know why she thought there might be — and the silence seemed profound. She didn't even hear any birds or other typical forest sounds. Only the thin whirring of the breeze through the upper branches of the surrounding trees disturbed the little cleared off area where Buck parked the SUV.

After helping her out, he retrieved his backpack and carefully put it to one side of a few chopped-off tree stumps which seemed to have been used as a work area of sorts. After getting his things settled to his satisfaction, he turned and held out a hand to Gail.

'Come on. It will be a lot cooler inside. You're not claustrophobic, are you?'

'Not much,' she replied. 'I've never been inside one of these, so I can't say for sure how I'll feel once we're in there. Does it go back very far?'

'It goes back in a ways, but you don't need to go in all the way. I can go check the different spots I've been keeping an eye on, but you can hang out near the front if you'd prefer.'

'Yeah. I'll probably do that. I'd hate to get back in there and start freaking out!'

She grinned, trying to make a joke of it.

'Okay, let's go. It's actually quite easy to walk right in. The corridor itself is pretty even, unless there's been some kind of erosion or wash-out. That's what I'll be checking for.' He reached out a hand to steady her and they entered the old shaft, Buck leading the way.

The first thing she noticed was how refreshing it felt after the somewhat humid heat just outside. She peered cautiously about, noting the rough-hewn walls created with a miner's axe. They hadn't gotten very far inside the cavern when Buck suddenly stopped.

'Darn it! I'm sorry,' he said. 'I went off and forgot the lanterns. We'll need them if we go in any further. There's no light source in there, and it'll be too dark to find our away around if we get in too deep. Just wait here for me. I'll be right back with the lamps.' He turned quickly and headed back toward the entrance.

Gail stood still and waited. She thought she was about 10 or 15 feet from the entrance and could just barely make out the contours of the walls surrounding her.

Then — suddenly — there was the muffled sound of an explosion — and all went black. Then the enveloping black had gotten even darker.

That must have been when she passed out. From oxygen deprivation? Perhaps, though she hoped not.

After regaining consciousness, the realization that she was trapped alone here in the dark was daunting. She began searching around blindly for her keychain with the tiny maglight dangling from it before deciding it must have fallen to the ground. *Pull it together, Gail*, she admonished herself. *You have to keep your head now. Think!*

Tentatively she brushed her hand further along the wall, then stopped. A tiny trickle of wetness moistened her fingertips.

Water! She would need water if she was going to survive. She licked her fingers greedily. Yes, it tasted fresh. It must be leaking into the mine from some underground spring. Now, what could she use to collect it? After a moment of thought she pulled the filmy green scarf from around her neck, crumpled it up, and stuffed it carefully into the crevasse. There. The scarf would slowly soak up the water — then she could squeeze it into her mouth, wipe her sweaty face with it, perhaps wrap it around her aching neck. It might be enough to keep her alive . . . for a while.

Next she stood quietly for a moment and thought. What was it Buck had said? This was one of the smaller mines in the area? Good. Maybe she could explore her options for escape without wandering around for days in a huge underground labyrinth. But how, in the dark, could she begin?

She understood that the greatest danger she faced was becoming confused and losing her bearings. She must not wander so far away from the entrance to the cavern that she would fail to hear possible rescuers . . . or that they would not be able to find her until it was too late.

But how to explore *without* losing her bearings, not to mention her one sure source of water?

Thoughtfully she fingered the four large decorative buttons running down the front of the light linen jacket she had thrown on for this excursion. Why not . . . yes, why not pace off a certain number of steps . . . fifty perhaps? Then tear off one of the buttons and put it in her right pocket. Another fifty paces . . . another button. She could actually move two hundred paces that way, and still keep track of how far she had gotten from the entrance.

To return, she would only need to come back fifty paces then move one button from her right pocket to her left. And so on. Yes, that might work. But how to be sure she wasn't veering off to the right or left of the main shaft? She would have to maintain her handhold on the wall to her right, the same wall she was leaning against now. Not ever take her hand off of it. Yes. Move slowly and methodically, fifty paces at a time, further into the cavern . . . just to see what the possibilities were.

She slipped her hand down into the jacket pocket, just to be sure there were no holes. What was this? She pulled out a scrunched-up granola bar. She felt in the other pocket, then greedily ripped off the top of the wrapper and bit into the hard surface of the dried-up bar. She crunched on the mass, chewing slowly, then swallowed. Carefully she rewrapped the rest of the bar and stuffed it back in her pocket. Better save the rest for later.

Now, to begin her exploration. She had been carrying only a small zippered bag with her ID and keys attached to her belt. She still had the bag, but the keys, with the tiny flashlight dangling from the chain, had fallen off or she had dropped them somewhere, and now they were lost. She made sure the bag was still hanging on her belt. It was important that she had her ID with her in case . . . in case she could not tell rescuers who she was.

Clinging to the side of the wall like some weird kind of spider, she put a trembling foot forward.

One, two, three . . . six, seven, eight... Soon she had reached twenty, but then stumbled forward and nearly fell when her foot struck up against a rock in the path. *Twenty-one? Or was it twenty-three?* She had lost count!

All right. Did it matter that much? Twenty? Or twenty-three? Two or three paces off would not matter much. But she couldn't make that mistake again. She began her slow process once more.

Twenty . . . Twenty-three, twenty-four, twenty-five...

By the time she reached fifty she was exhausted, between concentrating on counting, holding fast to the wall at her side, and being doubly careful now not to trip or fall over the occasional rock outcropping in the path. She stopped and leaned against the wall; then, fingering carefully the top jacket button, she grasped it firmly, twisted and it popped off in her hand. She stuffed it down in her pocket with the remains of the granola bar. Then breathed deeply for a few minutes, trying to still her pounding heart.

Funny. Her eyes seemed to be adjusting to the dark. She could almost make out the shapes of rocks and the curve of the wall ... *very* strange. She jerked to attention. Not funny at all. It might be her imagination, but it did appear that the inky blackness she had become accustomed to in her journey was a little greyer there, off to the left.

Could there be some *light* coming in from that direction? She passed her hand over her grimy brow . . . then stopped again. Wait. Did she feel a bit of air?

More alert now, she turned slightly and forced her gaze off to the left. Yes. There was definitely a light breath of air wafting in from that area. And the atmosphere seemed greyish, rather than cloaked in dark obscurity.

All right. She had come fifty paces. She knew that because she had one button in her pocket. Did she dare turn to the left here, cross the narrow corridor, then edge her way down what was obviously a branch off the main shaft, still holding to the right-hand wall? She forced her brain to conjure the possibilities. By doing that, would she lose her way for sure? Never be able to find her way back to the entrance — and that crucial water source?

No. She thought. *As long as I continue*

to count my paces and keep track of them, I should be able to go fifty paces or more down the offshoot, and still be able to find my way back to this spot. I have to try. It does look like there might possibly be another entrance or exit down that direction.

Of course! *Now* she remembered.

When she had glanced at the old drawings on display in the little mining office in town, she recalled clearly now that the Clarissa Mine — *the smallest one!* — had two entrances: one at each end of a sort of extended V shape. She had thought it was unusual at the time, but then had forgotten that detail until just now. And hadn't Buck confirmed that this was one of the smallest mines in the area? Could *this* be the Clarissa Mine?

With renewed energy, Gail resolutely moved across the narrow path and reached for the right side of the opening to the alternate route. It took her a while but she eventually identified the main opening to the second shaft and situated herself firmly against the right-hand wall. Glancing back into the utter darkness she had just left, she turned her head toward the grey aura ahead of her and began her second set of fifty paces.

As she moved steadily forward, one step at a time, she could feel the atmosphere lifting; could sense the air was a bit fresher here. And if it wasn't light enough to actually see clearly, the remaining dark was not as heavy, nor as dense. She actually began moving a bit more quickly and less tentatively, gaining confidence as she progressed toward the light.

Suddenly she got a whiff of something sweetish and musty-smelling. She paused and glanced down. There, in the middle of the pathway she was skirting, lay a mound of clothing or . . . something else. She started to move toward it, then reached back for the safety of the wall. No. She couldn't be distracted now. She had to keep moving steadily ahead. Besides, her intuition told her, she already knew what the sweet, musty-smelling heap of clothing was.

She had to free herself first. There would be time later to come back with others to make sure. Right now she had to keep moving forward . . . keep moving . . . forward . . . to . . . safety. Then, abruptly, the pathway ran out!

The passageway apparently ended here. Was there no way out after all?

Panting now, she clung to the side of the wall to steady herself as she peered anxiously about her in the now more lucid haze. She could barely make out a vague structure of sorts near the end of the wall. It appeared to be a metal bracket hanging precariously from the rocky façade. She moved close enough to examine it more carefully.

Was it a ladder of some sort? If so, she wondered if it was sturdy enough to actually hold someone scrambling toward the ceiling. She stepped to one side and gazed up as far as she could make out. Yes. It looked as though there was a turn near the top — and there was definitely more light coming through there.

She could also feel a steady stream of cool air wafting down through the tunnel. That had to be it. There must be some sort of opening around that bend in the corner of the ceiling.

She had now lost track of her paces. She knew she had come 150 steps into the depths of the cavern, including this branch section, because she had three buttons in her right-hand pocket. Beyond that she could not say. She had stopped counting, she realized, sometime after she had passed the foul mess on the floor of the tunnel.

Well, there was nothing left to do but soldier on as best she could. Her very life depended on what lay at the top of this tunnel.

She gripped the metal rung with purpose. She had to test that metal — as she tested her own mettle — to see if it could bear her weight. She was exhausted and wondered how in heaven's name she would find the strength to pull herself up, up, up towards the ceiling.

Resolutely, she took off her jacket and flung it over the rails above her head, careful not to disturb the pocket contents. Grabbing onto the bar tightly, with the jacket cushioning her battered hands, she pulled herself up onto the first rung, and hung there, like some wounded bird, gathering her resolution to continue. Gradually she moved her jacket on up to the next rung above her, grabbed hold and pulled — hard — again and again. She dare not look down into the black pit below her, afraid she would lose both her nerve and her equilibrium.

Over and over she repeated the process — tossing the jacket up and over the next rung, grabbing it and pulling with all her dwindling might, until she achieved purchase with quivering feet and legs onto the next rung up.

A sudden gust of air startled her and she hung on for dear life, struggling to maintain her unsteady balance, and frantic of losing either her tenuous footing or her wavering consciousness. She sniffed eagerly. The scent was of pine and sun, and the cool lick of breeze against her face refreshed and elated her. She must be near the top! One more push and freedom might be hers.

She hauled her weight up once more — and stopped in dismay. Although there was indeed light and air aplenty, wafting down from the ceiling, she saw nothing that looked like an actual exit of any sort. Pulling up closer, she realized what she should have surmised earlier.

There was an opening all right, but it was blocked off solidly by a heavy grate — *bolted to the steel plate supporting the ladder*!

Unless she could somehow pry that grate up, she was no better off here than she had been below — other than that she at least had some visibility and good clean air to breathe.

She got as close as she could to the grate and in the dim hazy light of an obscured sun, she tried to examine the bolts. She grabbed the main cross-piece of the grate and gave it a yank. It didn't budge and appeared to be solidly attached. What could she use? She thought. There was a metal buckle on the belt around her waist. Maybe she could use that to somehow pry one of the bolts loose. Enough, maybe, to force the grate up and back.

Quickly, breathing hard in her eagerness, she hooked one arm through the ladder upright; then as carefully as she could, she first removed her zipper bag from her belt and stuffed it down the front of her blouse, then carefully unfastened the belt buckle from around her waist. Scared to death she would drop it, she maneuvered the loosened belt away from her body and quickly slung it up and over the last rung at the top of the ladder.

She pushed herself up as near to the ceiling as she could and gingerly, leaving the belt looped over the rung, began to tap the buckle around the edge of the grate, searching for a spot weakened by rust, or any bolt that might have come loose from time and the elements.

Tap, tap, tap . . . slowly . . . slowly . . . she moved the buckle around the grate . . . back and forth . . . up and down. Wait! There! She felt a giving way beneath the buckle in her hand. One of the bolts *was* looser than the others. Perhaps a steady drip of water from outside had rusted it a bit more. She had no idea, but didn't care.

Now she worked in a frenzy, banging

away with the metal buckle at the rusty old bolt, the one thing now which stood between her and that great beautiful forest waiting outside. Finally, just as she was about to give up all hope, the bolt fell away from the grate, tumbling over and over past her on her rickety perch — down, down, down into that hellish netherworld below.

Elated, she paused to catch her breath and gather her strength for one last time. Steadying herself as best she could, with legs wrapped around the ladder rungs and uprights and using her jacket once more to protect her hands, she grabbed the two main cross pieces of the grate nearest the now-empty bolt hole and pushed with all her might. At first, nothing happened, and her elation turned quickly to despair as she realized that the grate might be so rusted onto the opening plate that there would be no way she could actually move it.

Push! Push! she ordered herself. *You have to keep pushing . . . you have no other choice now.* Then!

Suddenly there was a screeching sound

like something out of the bowels of hell, and the grate popped upward. Gail had to grab onto the ladder with both hands to avoid tumbling back and down into the pit beneath her. But — just as she was about to reach to pull herself up and out through the now open grate — she was horrified to see a man's large hand reaching down through the opening toward her.

'Fancy meetin' you here, Miz Norris,' a familiar voice rumbled. 'I figured you might try this . . . '

9

Grave Matters

'Ugh . . . ' Gail opened her eyes to blinding sun and breathed deeply of the fresh pinescented air. 'What . . . where am I?'

True to the *cliché*, she had lost her bearings completely. The last thing she remembered, before sinking into blessed darkness, was the sensation of two strong hands pulling her up and out of the pit.

After that, she had dreamed peacefully of sipping coffee with Connie at their familiar table back home, sharing the morning paper in their normal manner. But she wasn't back home — and this wasn't Connie assisting her to sit up and peering anxiously into her face.

'Hugo! Where did you come from? How . . . ?'

'Easy does it. Don't try to get up too fast.' Hugo patted her shoulder. 'You've had quite an ordeal, young lady. Why in the world did you go off with the Buckaroo man like that? I almost didn't make it in time to save the day!'

'I never suspected him. I thought it was Dunlap all the time.' She shook her head furiously. 'What a fool I've been!'

'Well, he had everyone around here fooled all right. They all thought he was just the nicest, most polite young man that could ever be. Little did they know they had a vicious pit bull in their midst. But . . . ' He gestured down the hill beyond them toward the front entrance to the mine. 'That's all over now. Where he's going, he won't see the light of day for a very long time.'

'But how in the world did you find me? I stumbled onto this exit purely by accident. It was pure luck.' Gail shook her head in frustration.

'Not so. Once I had figured out what Buck was all about, I began to look for you, to tell you what I'd discovered. When they told me at the mine office that you'd actually gone off with him for a tour of this mine, I took a good hard look at that diagram on the wall showing the layout. The girl in the office said she'd seen you studying it too, so I thought I'd better memorize it . . . just in case.'

'Well, I'm glad you did. I don't think I could have forced that grate off alone. It was rusted solid. But what made you think I might be following Buck into a trap?'

'There have been several of these incidents over the past few years. Unexpected cave-ins and such. There hasn't been any record of anyone found in any of them, so most of the time they just leave them as is, fence them off with a warning sign posted, and everyone just stays away. But the other interesting thing I noticed was the unusual number of young girls in the area who have gone missing, coincidentally — or maybe not so coincidentally — during the same period of time.

'A lot of the younger kids aren't exactly eager to hang around here forever, so nobody thinks too much of it. Bright lights, big city. They mostly just figure that the missing girls are probably runaways, off to see how the other half lives. As we've already noticed, even the authorities don't put too much effort into finding any of them. I'm willing to bet we'll find more than one of these missing 'runaways' down in these so-called accidental cave-ins. Trouble will be getting anyone to listen.

'I *was* able to convince the local authorities, once they showed up, to hold Buck for arraignment. I actually saw him light the charge that blew in the mine entrance. I tried to stop him, but I was just a little too late. He didn't get away, though.'

Gail looked over at the crowd of state troopers and emergency vehicles gathered down the hill next to the now-demolished mine entrance. There, with two brawny patrolmen on either side of him, stood Buck Brandon, hands pulled behind him in cuffs.

'I told them I saw him lead you in to the mine — a little white lie — then come back out and set the charge. By the time I tackled him, got him cuffed and called the state authorities, I'd convinced him to confess to me that he had lured you inside. Then — '

'He told me he had to come back outside to get some more lights,' Gail interposed.

'But he set the charge instead. I tied him to a tree after I cuffed him and tried like hell to get that entrance dug out, but without much in the way of tools, I could see it would take a crew to make any headway. Meanwhile, *you* were trapped inside. I had no idea if he had knocked you out, or whatever.'

'I don't think so. I did lose consciousness for a minute or two after the explosion. I think it was the shock of it . . . or maybe oxygen deprivation. But I wasn't really injured. When I came to, I just tried to use my head and think what to do. I have no idea how long I was in there.'

'Not as long as it probably seemed to you. By the time I got Buck squared away and the authorities had started to arrive, I ran straight up here to the top of the hill to try and find that second opening. I had just started working on the grate from the top when I saw your fingers poking out. Thank God it wasn't any longer than that.'

'So they're holding him on . . . ?

'Attempted murder. With your testimony and mine, there won't be any doubt about it.'

'There's more, Hugo. There's much more.' She grabbed his arm. 'There's something else in there, down at the bottom of the mine. Hugo, I think I may have found Sonia . . . ' Her voice trailed off and tears began to trickle from her scrunched-up eyes. 'But I'm afraid we were too late.'

Hugo shook his head and patted her arm in consolation. 'Will you be all right to stay here just a moment?'

She nodded.

'Just rest if you can while I go get some help.' He headed down the hill and, as Gail watched, he got the attention of the trooper in charge. He spoke earnestly to the authority for a few minutes, gesturing back up towards Gail. The man shook his head in disbelief, then called several more men to his side and gave them instructions.

is way back to her, side doors on one of rked nearby opened and several cadaver dogs and their handlers bounced out, the hounds howling joyfully at being freed from their confinement. Soon, the lead trooper was kneeling beside Gail and asking her to carefully repeat to him what she had told Hugo.

'It's on the floor of the mine shaft,' she said, trying to visualize the spot in her mind. 'It's about . . . ' She fingered the buttons in her pocket. 'I think it's between 50 to 100 paces back into the mine from the bottom of this ladder.' She gestured at the yawning mouth of the pit with its rusted grate hanging uselessly to one side. 'But they can't miss it . . . there's an odor . . . ' Her face crumpled again and she collapsed back to the ground.

'Is it all right if I get her down to the ambulance?' Hugo said. 'I think she's about spent.'

The trooper nodded and signaled to the other men gathering nearby. 'Get this lady down to the ambulance,' he shouted, '*now!* Don't stand around like you don't know what you're supposed to be doing. She needs treatment.'

'Hugo?' She grabbed at him desperately, as the men formed a makeshift cradle of their arms to carry her. 'Hugo? Have you called Connie? Please call Connie . . . '

'I already did, Gail. He and Charles are on their way. They should be landing in Grass Valley in a few hours. Don't worry. He'll be here soon.'

★　★　★

Gail was resting quietly on an uncomfortable gurney in E.R. with heart rate and blood pressure monitors beeping steadily beside her and an intravenous lead dripping revitalizing fluids into her arm, when Connie and Charles peered around the large canvas curtain dividing her cubicle from her neighbor's.

Connie leaned over and kissed her soundly, ignoring all the little things standing in his way. Hugo had already informed him on the way in that Gail was in good shape, in spite of her ordeal, and would be allowed to leave with them as soon as one of the on-duty physicians had a chance to review and release her.

'Never again,' he muttered, patting her hand. 'We're never going to get involved in such a stunt again.'

'But Connie,' Gail said, her eyes glistening with unshed tears. 'We *found* her! I know it was too late, but at least we know what happened to her, And that sick monster is behind bars — hopefully for the rest of his life. If we hadn't at least tried, no one would ever have known what had happened to her . . . and all those other poor girls as well.'

The local authorities at Duneville by now had requested additional assistance from the State of California, and an all-out effort was in progress to excavate all of the other caved-in mines in the area and search them thoroughly. Gail had no doubt there would be many more grisly remains recovered in the process. At least those girls' families could at last deal with their losses properly.

10

Order in the Court

The old Justice Court in Nevada City smelled of an unhappy mix of furniture polish, musty body odor — and fear. As portly old Judge Fogg entered and took his seat, the bailiff called the packed room to order. Connie rose from his place next to the district attorney at the prosecutor's table.

'Your Honor, I'd like to address the court,' he began.

'And you are . . . ?'

'I am Conrad Osterlitz of the legal firm of Osterlitz and Brevard, based in Cathcart. These are my colleagues and partners, Ms. Gail Brevard and Mr. Charles Walton.' He nodded at the two seated just behind the rail. 'We are all authorized to practice law in the states of California, Nevada and Arizona, as well as at our home office. You have before you our credentials.'

The judge glanced down at his desk and carefully perused the documents before him. 'Go on,' he said, apparently satisfied with the validity of their licenses, and nodding in Connie's direction.

'I would like to enter a brief of *amicus curiae* in the action before you pertaining to the arraignment of William Brandon preparatory to the *State of California vs. William Brandon*. I have discussed this matter thoroughly with District Attorney Bellows, and he concurs.' He paused and looked at his notes.

'In addition to the testimony of Ms. Brevard *née* Norris, who has been acting in an undercover capacity here for the last two weeks — ' He again nodded towards Gail. ' — I would like also to call, with the court's permission, Mr. Hugo Goldthwaite, a private investigator in the employ of Osterlitz and Brevard, who has been shadowing her and conducting investigations of his own into the activities of the aforesaid William Brandon, known locally as Buck Brandon. I may also, at some point, call one or two other witnesses, if the court is willing.'

'And may I ask what was the purpose of this private investigation undertaken without the knowledge or permission of the local authorities?' Judge Fogg glared at Connie over the top of his gold-rimmed glasses. 'Seems to me to have been a reckless if not downright illegal undertaking, to say the least.' He har-rumphed and settled back in his swivel chair, waiting for Connie's response.

'Your Honor, with all due respect to both the court *and* the local authorities, all such avenues had been approached with no success before the decision was made to conduct an undercover opera-tion, *with all the legal authority we required*, on our own. May I explain?' he added hastily, before the judge had time to interrupt again.

'By all means, explain away,' the magistrate responded huffily.

'Very well. Our firm was approached several weeks ago by our client, Mr. Nicholas Quintaine, a citizen of good standing in the city of San Francisco, and his *protégé*, Miss Marilee Hudson, also of San Francisco. They were concerned when a close friend of Miss Hudson's, Sonia Mattingly, went missing without explanation. Miss Mattingly had been an acquaintance of Miss Hudson since childhood, and both she and Mr. Quintaine were convinced that it was out of character for her to simply leave the area and disappear without leaving word with someone at home.

'Miss Hudson was aware that Miss Mattingly had applied for, and had been accepted for, a position of summer employment in the community of Cooleyville. She had informed Miss Hudson of her plans, and had left by bus to make the trip from the Bay Area to Cooleyville early last month. She promised to inform Miss Hudson of her safe arrival there. When no word was forthcoming, Miss Hudson became concerned and began making enquiries of her own. She first attempted to contact the proposed employer, Mr. Frank Dunlap.'

A gasp was heard from the crowd and heads craned to stare at Frank, who was sitting about halfway back with a shocked look on his face.

'He claimed Miss Mattingly had never

arrived, and that he knew nothing about her safety or whereabouts.'

Another communal gasp was heard.

Connie went on. 'You have before you a copy of the advertisement which appeared in the Bay Area *Penny-Saver* on May 15th, and again on June 1st.'

Again the judge glanced down at the documents before him and nodded.

'I object!' came a shout. Frank stood and shook his fist at Connie and the prosecutor's team in general. 'I object to this attempt to screw me! I never saw the woman . . . as for this Gail Norris, or whatever her name is, I object to her coming into my house under false pretenses like that. She had no right! *No right at all!*'

'Shut up Frank, and *sit down!*' Judge Fogg shouted. 'You don't have any right to object. This isn't your case, and you're not your own attorney! I don't want to hear another word out of you, or you'll be ushered out. *Understood?*' The judge knew Frank Dunlap, and not just by reputation. He had a feeling this was going to be a long and difficult day, and he was in no mood to coddle idiots.

Frank took his seat, still seething, but silent once more. Several sympathizers around him reached over to give him a pat of encouragement on the back, but others sat back with an 'I told you so' attitude visible on self-satisfied faces. Frank wasn't popular with everyone in the town, and several thought it was long past time for his comeuppance.

'All right, Mr. Osterlitz, I'm listening. What other attempts were made to find the missing young woman?'

'First, the firm accepted the petition of Mr. Quintaine and Miss Hudson to take on the task of trying all possible avenues to find her friend. After lengthy discussions with the both of them, we determined that there indeed seemed to be a sinister cast to her disappearance. Miss Mattingly was responsibly employed as a school teacher, owned and lived in the home that had once belonged to her now-deceased parents, and was, to all reports, an upstanding citizen of the highest character. It was totally unlike her to be so irresponsible as to go off without telling her friends her plans.

'At that point, Mr. Goldthwaite was asked to begin making the same enquiries Miss Hudson had attempted, but this time with his expertise and skills acquired through long experience of tracking persons missing either by their own design, or by foul play. His discussions with the authorities in the Cooleyville area, such as they are, given the size of the town and its relative isolation, came to naught. The sheriff's substation at Duneville either could not, or refused, to conduct any kind of search or inquiry of their own. Everyone kept saying there was absolutely no proof that the young woman had actually gotten on that bus in the Bay Area and got off hours later in Cooleyville. She had simply vanished.' He paused to sip from the water bottle at his place on the table.

'But Mr. Osterlitz, how could you be sure she *had* actually gotten on that bus? Couldn't she have changed her mind at the last minute? By all accounts she was an independent person of normal intelligence. Didn't she have the right to go off on her own without well-meaning friends following to check up on her?'

The audience murmured in agreement at the judge's words, which seemed reasonable enough to them.

'One would think so, Your Honor.' Connie paused a moment. 'And so it might have remained, if it were not for one thing.'

'Which is . . . ?' Now the courtroom was deadly silent.

'We *know* she was on the tour bus from Sacramento to Cooleyville.'

'Because?' The silence was so palpable that a fly buzzing around the ceiling fan could be heard droning above it all.

'Because there *is* a witness. Mr. Goldthwaite, as I have said, is persistent and very experienced in such matters. He was able to obtain a list of the tour bus riders on that particular route on that particular day. With some difficulty he began tracking them all down to question them, one by one, about what they had seen and heard. There is at least one person, and possibly others, who not only witnessed Sonia Mattingly get on that bus in Sacramento, but who spoke with her during the journey. She even mentioned she was on her way to a summer job, and was looking forward to the change of scene.'

A murmur rose from the room, but was quickly gaveled silent. Connie cleared his throat and went on. 'When the bus got to Cooleyville, the individual who had spoken with her along the way got out briefly to buy souvenirs in the general store, but got back on immediately because she was going on to Duneville and didn't want to get left behind. She knows that Sonia got off the bus, but she didn't see what happened after that. Sonia was probably picked up at the drop-off point, if not by Mr. Dunlap, then by some other unknown person or persons. In the mix of all the usual tourists, she would hardly have been noticed by most of the citizens who, we presume, were simply going about their daily business.'

'I object, Your Honor. Hearsay,' began young Mr. Botts, attorney for the defense.

'Your Honor, if you will examine page

7 in the documents we have provided you — ' Connie gestured toward the papers already delivered to the judge's bench. ' — you will see we have a sworn affidavit from the aforementioned witness, Ms. Africa Jones. Ms. Jones could not be here today because of a family emergency, but the statement she gave to Mr. Goldthwaite in front of notarized witnesses attests to the accuracy of her identification of Miss Mattingly.'

The judge paged through the file until he reached page 7, perused it carefully, then set it to one side. 'This document appears to be in order,' he announced. 'Objection denied.'

'Thank you, Your Honor,' Botts said. 'Will you stipulate that my objection be noted for a possible appeal?'

The judge nodded. 'So ordered.' Botts returned to his seat, obviously frustrated by this unexpected turn of events.

Buck Brandon, in orange prisoner attire and with a guard at his side, sat at the defense table staring stoically straight ahead, oblivious to all around him.

Gail glanced at him and noted the hint

of a healing black eye, and his lip looked as if it had been cut. She wondered if he was being held in the general population of the small local prison. Even prisoners did not look kindly on serial abusers or murderers.

The courtroom remained eerily silent, except for the persistent buzzing of the flies overhead. Gail brushed away a drop of perspiration from her brow and waited. There would be more.

'I think it's time for an adjournment,' the judge said, breaking the silence. 'All parties to this action will be back here in two hours, no exceptions.' This time no one objected at all, and the court was quickly cleared.

★   ★   ★

'Court come to order; all rise,' called out the bailiff as Judge Fogg proceeded onto the bench. Once he had settled his bulk into his sagging padded swivel chair, the bailiff added, 'Please be seated. Court is now in session.'

The magistrate busied himself for a few

moments, rustling through the papers on his desk and taking a sip of water before peering over his spectacles at the prosecutor's table. 'Mr. Osterlitz, you had the floor when we adjourned. Are you planning to call any more witnesses?'

'Yes, Your Honor. I would like to call Hugo Goldthwaite to the stand.'

There was a little murmur of expectation as a guard left the room to retrieve the husky P.I. waiting in the hall. He was quickly sworn in and once seated in the witness stand, turned expectantly toward Connie.

'Please give us your full name and occupation and a brief summary of your connection to this case,' Connie prompted him.

'My name is Hugo Goldthwaite, Jr., co-owner of the Goldthwaite Detective Agency in Cathcart. My firm has worked on retainer with Osterlitz and Brevard for approximately 8 years in various capacities. In this particular instance, my duties were to provide backup for Ms. Brevard in her undercover role as an employee of Mr. Frank Dunlap in Cooleyville. I was on the same bus she took from Sacramento to Cooleyville and shadowed her closely throughout her stay there. In addition, I undertook investigations of my own into a series of seemingly unrelated events which, I believe, formed a pattern of foul play.'

'Can you describe those events for us?'

'Objection.' Botts rose from his seat again. 'I don't see what connection these so-called 'events' have with the case against my client.'

'Your Honor, I believe if you will allow Mr. Goldthwaite to relate to you what he has discovered, the connection will be clear.'

'Objection denied,' growled the judge. The courtroom spectators sighed in relief. Curiosity aroused to a man, they wanted to hear the whole story.

'Thank you, Your Honor.' Connie turned smoothly back to Hugo. 'Now, Mr. Goldthwaite. What was the nature of your enquiries, and what did you discover in the process of your investigations?'

'Once Ms. Brevard was settled into the Dunlap household, I took a room over the old tavern in the middle of town. I began to talk to the locals casually, leading them into conversation about things that had happened in the area that seemed odd or out of place to them. There were two common threads of events that had happened over time which had taken a huge toll in the community.'

'And what were those two common threads that you began to discern during your stay in the town?' Connie nodded encouragingly. The narrative was going well.

'First, for at least ten years, the town's young people — teenagers, or a little older — had been disappearing, leaving no word of where they were going or why. The authorities almost always assumed that they were runaways. The theory was that these youngsters had simply grown tired of the isolated life in a small town and had gone off to see the world. Even when their parents or guardians swore that it was totally out of character for them to have done so.'

The crowd began whispering and mumbling urgently to each other until

Judge Fogg gave a sharp rap with his gavel. Hugo cleared his throat and went on. 'What caught my attention about these disappearances — for that is what I firmly believe they were — is that almost all of those who disappeared were women. So far as I could discover, during that entire time there were only two or three young men who went missing, and they all had juvenile criminal records — thus a motive for making themselves scarce.'

'I see,' said Connie, looking about the courtroom as if he too, was curious about what Hugo had discovered. 'And what was the second common thread which you unraveled in your searches?'

'During the same period of time, and corresponding almost eerily with the so-called runaways, there began to be more and more frequent accidents associated with the old mines in the area — cave-ins, explosions, wash-outs — you name it, whatever could happen in an old mine began happening on a regular basis. There was almost always a short lapse of time between the disappearance of a young woman and an accidental cave-in, but the events were close enough together I wonder that the townspeople didn't take note of it.'

Botts sprang to his feet at this point. 'Your Honor, I object most strenuously to this particular line of questioning. The witness is conjecturing here, and Counsel is encouraging him in this outlandish speculation. What proof does he have of such a wild tale?' He stood panting and clinging to his table like a life raft. Clearly Mr. Botts was out of his league against the more experienced Connie.

'Mr. Osterlitz? Is there any proof of a connection between these seemingly unrelated events? I tend to agree with Mr. Botts that this is beginning to sound like a fantasy — not a factual investigation.'

'The state police, as we speak, on the strength of both Mr. Goldthwaite's evidence and the events of June 30th, have begun detailed examinations of all unexplained mine accidents and cave-ins going back ten years. At the same time, they are attempting to document the identities of all the young girls who went missing during that time. I think if I may have a little leeway here to provide background, we can and will make our case against Mr. Brandon.

'He returned to this area just about ten years ago, straight out of college. We're trying to figure out what his record looked like before then, but regardless, this most recent incident — the attempted assassination of Ms. Brevard — would seem to confirm a pattern with him, one which is most sinister indeed.

'We are, by listing the chronology of events, attempting to show clearly what might have happened to many of the town's missing young people. Surely . . . ' He glanced about the room. 'Surely these good people would like to know the truth about their loved ones' fate.'

This time the murmur rose to the level of a low roar and one or two individual voices could be heard crying out, 'Yes, Judge. Please let them go on. We *need* to know the truth!'

Gail looked back and saw Winnie sitting several rows back, a shocked look on her face and tears streaming down her face. Could her husband have been one of the victims too? Had he discovered what had happened to *their* daughter and paid the ultimate price for that discovery?

The judge sat in silence for a moment before responding. Finally he lifted his hooded eyes to Connie's, and in that instant Connie knew he had won — everything. 'Very well, Mr. Osterlitz,' Fogg rumbled. 'You may proceed.'

'Thank you, Your Honor.' Connie turned back to Hugo. 'Now, Mr. Goldthwaite. I want you to move to the afternoon of June 30th and tell us, in your own words, what you witnessed at the old Clarissa Mine site near Beaver Creek.'

Hugo glanced at his notes, then began. 'With the court's permission, I would like to lay some groundwork for the decisions I made on June 30th.' He glanced at Fogg, who nodded and waved him on. 'As I said previously, I had become concerned about the 'coincidental' nature of events which had taken place in and near the Cooleyville area for the past ten years. When I realized that the defendant . . . ' He paused to look in the direction of

Buck Brandon. 'When I learned that he had returned to this area within that time frame, I began to look into his background.

'At first, everything seemed normal. He was an average young man who had grown up in the fairly isolated village of Pine Cone. His parents were out of the picture, and by all accounts he was pretty much a loner during his childhood, by choice as much as by circumstance. He lived with his grandmother during the summers, but once he started school, he was boarded out in Nevada City, there being no public school available where his grandmother resided.'

'Objection.' Botts stood and addressed the court. 'I see no relevance to this at all, Your Honor. The defense is willing to stipulate that Mr. Brandon grew up in this area, went away to school, then returned at some point to 'give back' to the community where he was raised. If the *amicus curiae* has anything at all to reveal about Mr. Brandon's background, then he should get to the point and stop wasting the court's time.'

Judge Fogg pursed his lips and considered. 'Mr. Osterlitz?'

'Your Honor, we believe that an understanding of Mr. Brandon's background will reveal a pattern that is consistent with the events which took place on June 30th, and we beg the court's indulgence in allowing Mr. Goldthwaite to explain how his discoveries led him to the Clarissa Mine that fateful day in time to prevent further tragedy.'

'Very well, I'll allow it. But please — ' He looked sternly at Hugo. ' — try to be as concise as possible.'

'Yes, Your Honor.' Hugo paused to gather his thoughts. 'To make a long story shorter, from grammar school on, William Brandon was not only a good student; by all reports he was an excellent student. He excelled, especially in language arts, reading and writing. His teachers said his compositions were generally well-written and imaginative — 'fanciful, almost' was the way one of his instructors put it.

'At the same time, there was a dark side to young William. While his grades were good throughout — good enough to earn him a scholarship to the State University at Humboldt — he began to show a pattern of bullying and abuse towards younger and weaker children, particularly young girls. He was suspended several times for these infractions, but somehow he always managed to talk his way out of being expelled. It appears that his various teachers chose to pass him along to the next grade, mainly to get him out of their own classes.

'The teachers I spoke with who recalled him said that he was 'charming' and even 'likeable,' but they also said he could be devious and even dangerous unless he was monitored closely. There were a few reports of dead or maimed animals found in and around the homes where he boarded, but those allegations were never followed up, so that element is inconclusive.

'By the time young William had graduated from high school and headed off to Humboldt, the educators in Nevada City were generally glad to be clear of him.

'Next I queried various people at the university. Because of privacy issues, and also because of the passage of time, William's records there are a bit blurred. Again he made good grades, kept himself and, eventually, graduated honorably with a degree in engineering. Nobody really remembered him and he had apparently stayed out of trouble, so there were no criminal records for him in the system.

'I decided to take another tack. After introducing myself to the local sheriff's office near campus and telling them what I was seeking, they agreed to allow me to research their old files having to do with crimes or disturbances committed on and around the university. Limiting myself to the years when Brandon resided there, I quickly discovered a disturbing pattern. Both in the year prior to his matriculation, and in the year immediately following his graduation, when we know he had moved back to Cooleyville, there were few, if any, violent crimes against women recorded by the local authorities at Humboldt and its environs. But during the four years or so that Brandon was a resident there, there were a series of incidents filed which caught my eye.

'During Brandon's first year there were, perhaps, five or six complaints involving a so-called 'Kissing Bandit' who operated in the evening study hours on the upper floors of the library, where students often congregated to study late and prepare for their papers and exams. No real harm was done, but the women involved had been deeply frightened by what had happened to them. In each case the victim had been seated in a study carrel, engrossed in her books, when suddenly a tall man of slender but muscular build, disguised by a hood over his head and wearing nondescript clothing, entered from behind, grabbed the woman and forced her into an embrace which lasted for several minutes before taking his leave.

'Since 'no harm was done' in each of these cases, there was little follow-up beyond interviewing other students and the handful of librarians on duty about what they might have noticed. No arrests were ever made, nor was the perpetrator ever identified.

'Then a more sinister aspect began to appear. In the second year Brandon was there, at least twelve separate incidents of inappropriate and even abusive behavior toward various women students were recorded by both the campus police and the local authorities. These attacks were much more violent in nature and included both violations of a sexual nature and, even worse, several of the women were struck on the back of the head or thrown into walls or furniture, resulting in mild to severe injuries. There were no deaths, however, and again the officials from both the school and the town were unable to find the culprit.

'These vicious attacks continued throughout Brandon's third year on campus. Not only that, but several missing persons reports were filed, all of young women. Just as has happened here, most often there would be a cursory investigation then the concerned parents or friends were told that most likely the student had tired of her classes and had just 'taken off.' Most of the young ladies were of age, so there was very little the university or town police could do to follow up.

'Then in the first term following the Christmas holiday of his senior year, tragedy struck. There was a fire in one of the women's dorms — arson by all accounts — and three young women died when they found themselves trapped in their room because the outer door was blocked from the outside. A thorough examination of the room revealed not only accelerant on the floor near the door, but the windows leading to a fire escape had been jammed shut. In the excitement and smoke generated by the fire, there was no way those girls could have escaped. This time the investigation was long and thorough — but once again *no suspect was ever caught*.

'It is my theory that the so-called 'Kissing Bandit' was a student at the university who escalated his activities from what could be called 'harmless pranks' to a much more violent level during his time on campus. Then, at the end of that fourth year, the attacks

154

suddenly ceased and the authorities concluded that the villain had completed his studies and moved away. The people I spoke with there were chagrined at their failure to find the man responsible for all those attacks — but they all seemed to be relieved that he was no longer operating in their jurisdiction.'

'Your Honor,' Botts bleated, 'I still don't see what any of this fairytale has to do with the action at hand. All of this is just hearsay and conjecture.'

'Overruled!' drummed out Fogg. 'Get on with your story, Mr. Goldthwaite. You have *me* curious now.'

'Thank you, Your Honor. It took me the better part of several days to get that information from the various sources at Humboldt. But when I realized what the pattern might mean, I immediately tried to reach Ms. Brevard to inform her of my findings — and to warn her.'

'Warn her?' Fogg peered over the bench at Hugo. 'Why did you think you needed to warn her?'

'Because I knew from my several conversations with her that she was looking at one or two other individuals as possibly involved in Miss Mattingly's disappearance and had not mentioned Brandon as a suspect. I also knew that she had struck up a friendly acquaintanceship with him and had had more than one discussion with him about the ramifications of the fire and Idy's death. I wanted to warn her to steer clear of the man until we could be sure what we were dealing with. The last thing I wanted was for her to go off on her own with him. I didn't trust him.'

'Go on,' the judge said, nodding thoughtfully. 'Continue your story.'

'Thank you. I couldn't reach Gail on her cell phone and thought either it had lost its charge or that she had turned it off for some reason. I thought her safety was more important at that point than protecting her true identity, so I headed up the hill to the Dunlap house to see if I could find her. The people there said she had been given a free afternoon and Mr. Brandon had invited her to stop in at the mining office to look over some old historical items.

'I ran back down there only to discover that Brandon had taken Ms. Brevard on a tour of one of the old mines. The girl in the office said that she had seemed particularly interested in the Clarissa Mine, which had been established by old Joe Dunlap and was named for his wife, Clarissa, known to most folks as Granny Dunlap.

'The receptionist pointed out a diagram of the mine on the wall and said Gail — Ms. Brevard — had been looking at it closely when Brandon had made his offer. I took a careful look at it too and noticed right away that it was unusual in that it had two apparent entrances. I made a little drawing of it, noted how to get there, and headed out to look for them.

'Frank Dunlap was in the tavern and he agreed to loan me his jeep.' He nodded toward a much-subdued Frank, sitting in the audience. 'I drove as close to the main entrance to the Clarissa as I dared, parked the jeep in a small grove of trees where it couldn't be seen, then crept forward until I could see and hear what was going on.

'At first, I saw only Brandon's car parked behind a large pine tree some distance from the entrance to the mine. I could hear voices echoing from the cavern which I recognized as Ms. Brevard's speaking with a man whom I took to be Brandon. A few minutes later, as I watched, Brandon emerged and went straight to pick up a backpack which he retrieved from the work area near the entrance to the mine.

'When I realized what he might be doing, I ran toward him, but I was too late. Before I could reach the area, he had placed the pack in the mineshaft entrance and began running back toward his car. I intercepted him just as the bomb exploded. I was horrified to see the entrance completely caved in and I knew Ms. Brevard was still inside!'

Gasps of shock and surprise erupted in the court, but quickly stopped as people leaned forward to hear the rest of Hugo's story.

'I tackled and subdued Mr. Brandon and tied him to a tree as quickly as possible, then called 911 to get help on the way. In a matter of minutes I began pawing and digging madly at the debris blocking entry to the mine, but I saw quickly that it was impossible to do it alone without tools.

'I called out several times but there was no response. I thought that either Ms. Brevard was too far underground to hear me, or . . . ' Hugo looked down as if recalling what that helplessness had felt like. ' . . . or she might have been injured or knocked unconsciousness by the explosion.

'In either case, I knew time was critical and I had to try to get her out of there as quickly as possible. Luckily I remembered the little diagram I had made in the mining office. I was able to tell right away where the second entrance was likely to be — around and up a slight hillside. I questioned Brandon briefly about why in the world he had done such a heinous thing and having gotten a confession from him that his intention had indeed been to 'shut that b — up!' — which, by the way, I was able to record . . . '

Connie sensed, rather than saw Botts slump in defeat.

'. . . I checked his restraints again, then set out to find the second entrance. It took maybe twenty or thirty minutes to make my way up the hill, poke about in the brush and clear a spot above the grating welded to the access point. By that time, thankfully, Gail — Ms. Brevard — had recovered sufficiently to explore her surroundings and get her bearings.

'She, too, recalled the diagram of the mine and set about to find the second entrance. She had just managed to crawl up to the surface when I had finally pried the grate loose. By the time I pulled her out and she realized she was safe, the county and state officials had begun to arrive. The rest, I think, most of you know.'

'Thank you, Mr. Goldthwaite. I have no more questions for you at this time.' Connie looked at the judge.

'Mr. Botts? Cross?'

'No, Your Honor.' Botts stood and glanced to one side at Buck Brandon, who still made no sign that he was aware of what was taking place around him.

'I do question, however, the legitimacy of Mr. Goldthwaite's elicitation of a so-called 'confession' from my client. But I will reserve my objections for a possible appeal.'

'Mr. Osterlitz? Do you have any more witnesses?'

'Yes, Your Honor. I would like to call at this time Ms. Gail Brevard to the stand.'

Heads craned as Gail stood and walked from her seat behind the prosecutor's table to the witness stand. After she was sworn in, she took her seat and waited for Connie to begin.

'Would you give your full name and occupation to the court, and a little background on how you came to be involved in this action?'

'My name is Gail Norris Brevard. I am a senior partner in the firm of Osterlitz and Brevard in Cathcart. I am here testifying today because that man . . . ' She pointed at Buck. 'The man seated there known as William 'Buck' Brandon tried to kill me on June 30th at the Clarissa Mine near Cooleyville.'

Connie paused for effect. The entire court hung on every word. 'And do you believe this death attempt was premeditated?'

'Objection!' called out Botts in desperation. 'Calls for a conclusion by the witness.' He was well aware that premeditation was one of the requirements for a first degree verdict, and that California was a death penalty state.

'Overruled,' replied Fogg, almost routinely at this point.

'Thank you,' Connie said automatically. 'Proceed, Ms. Brevard.'

'It is my firm belief that Mr. Brandon lured me to the Clarissa Mine with the full intention of either killing me or doing great bodily harm. No other conclusion can be made of his actions that day.'

'Now, Ms. Brevard,' Connie continued, 'please tell us, in your own words, just what happened when you arrived at the Clarissa Mine.'

Gail took her time, but was concise in her descriptions and tried to depict the events as they occurred in chronological order. When she got to the part about finding the decomposing body, however, all hell broke loose in the courtroom; and the judge, after gaveling furiously for a few minutes, asked the bailiff to escort out anyone who didn't 'sit down and shut up' immediately. After that, silence ensued once more and Gail finished the story of her rescue by Hugo with no further interruption.

'Thank you, Ms. Brevard. That will be all.' Connie turned toward Botts who, started to rise, then fell back in his seat.

'I have no questions for this witness, Your Honor,' the defense attorney said in resignation.

'Very well. Are you resting, Mr. Osterlitz? Does the district attorney have anything further?' He looked at the prosecutor who, up to this time, had maintained his silence and had not interfered with Connie's conduct of the trial.

'We have one more witness we'd like to call,' responded Connie. 'And, reminding the court of her qualifications, and if there is no objection, I would like the interrogation to be conducted by my colleague, Ms. Brevard.'

'Very well,' Fogg said. 'Call your witness.'

'At this time we would like to call Mr. James Dunlap.' The bailiff strode towards the double doors at the back of the room and the onlookers could hardly contain themselves when Cousin Jimmy Dunlap entered and made his way down the aisle. He was wearing his Sunday-best black suit, his skimpy grey hair had been combed neatly over the bald spot at the back of his head, and his ever-present cherubic smile was plastered just as firmly on his stubbly face.

He carefully climbed up to the witness box, then solemnly took his oath to 'tell the truth and nothing but the truth' before edging down into the seat. He was almost too short to look out over the top of the box, but his eyes gleamed alertly. For one of the few times in his life, he was the center of attention, and he drank it in like mother's milk.

Gail stood up and smiled at him. Since he smiled perpetually, it was difficult to tell if he was reacting to her warmth in a positive way. Still, she nodded at him in encouragement and began. 'Could you tell us your full name and where you are now residing?'

'Yes, ma'am. My name is James Franklin Dunlap. But most people call me Jimmy.

Just Jimmy. Or in Frank's case, Cousin Jimmy.' He spoke eagerly and nodded at Frank, looking on in bemusement. This was clearly his moment to shine. 'I live in Frank's house. My cousin Frank's house, on Hangover Hill, in Cooleyville. Well, it isn't *really* Hangover Hill. That's just a name they made up. But everyone knows it like that and everyone knows where it is.'

'Thank you, Jimmy. May I call you Jimmy?' He nodded vigorously. 'Well then, Jimmy. Can you recall a day in early June when you had gone down to the post office to pick up the mail for the family?'

'Yes, ma'am. I go *every* week . . . but *this* day was *special*!' His rheumy eyes glittered, both with moisture from his chronic glaucoma, and with glee at being the center of attention for once.

'I object, Your Honor.' Botts rose to challenge. 'Is Counsel claiming that this witness . . . ' He glanced at Jimmy in disdain. ' . . . that this so-called *witness* is going to tell us anything of value?'

'Your Honor,' Gail said, 'if the Court will allow Mr. Dunlap to continue, I'm sure the value of his testimony will become crystal-clear.' She allowed herself to fix Botts with her best scornful glare.

'Yes, I think I'll allow it,' Fogg said wearily. He was beginning to tire of all this back-and-forth parrying, and was inclined at this point to let the whole damn thing play itself out. He, too, glared sourly at poor Botts who, after all, was only trying to do his job.

'Very well. Now, Jimmy, can you tell us *why* this particular day in June was so special to you?'

'Yes, ma'am. You see, it was my *birth-day* . . .' The grin widened, Cheshire-style, until it threatened to take over the little man's whole face. 'And being that it was my birthday, Frank gave me ten dollars to go over into the general store and buy whatever I wished . . . once I had picked up the mail of course.' He sat back and waited.

'Your birthday! So of course you would remember such a special day. Now, think carefully, Jimmy. This next part is very important. Was there anything else *special* about that day? Something that stands out to you as being out of the ordinary?'

'Objection . . . leading the witness.' Botts, whose many objections had now all been overruled by Judge Fogg, had little hope of succeeding with this one — still he was not going to give up without a fight.

'Overruled,' came the by now expected response.

Gail shuffled her papers. 'It's all right for you to continue your story, Jimmy. What else was special about that particular day?'

'Well, that *girl* seemed special to me. She was as pretty as anything, and when she got off the tour bus, with all those other passengers milling around, in and out of the store, and across the road over to the tavern . . . and the Cooley monument . . . well, I just couldn't take my eyes off her. So I watched to see what she'd do — whether she was going to get back on the bus with the other passengers, or if she was going to stay here in Cooleyville.' All the unaccustomed talking had made his throat dry, and he paused to sip at the water bottle sitting in front of him on the desk.

'So this girl who got off the bus on your

birthday — which is June 5th, isn't it, according to your State of California DMV I.D.? This pretty girl caught your eye, so you watched her?'

'Yes ma'am. I didn't mean no harm, ma'am. I never would . . . hurt someone like that . . . '

'That's all right, Jimmy. We don't think you did.'

Botts moved restlessly in his chair but kept his silence.

'We just want to know what you actually saw that day, in connection with that particular girl. Did you watch long enough to see where she went?'

'Yes, ma'am, I did. I had picked up the mail and was fixing to wander over to the store and see what I might buy with my ten dollars. I thought maybe I could find a good pocket knife — one of those Swiss Army ones, you know? My old one has a chipped blade on it . . . ' His eyes wandered back out into the courtroom, as if he was looking for affirmation for his choice in purchases.

'But you didn't actually go into the store, did you, Jimmy?' Gail steered him back to the question at hand. 'Can you tell the court where you stopped to watch the girl after she got off the bus?'

'There's a little hallway between the post office and the general store. It's all part of the same building, so people don't have to get out into the weather when it's snowing or raining.'

'Yes, I know where that spot is. You can see out onto the street and walkway from there, but it would be hard for someone to see in, wouldn't it?'

'Oh, nobody could see you in there . . . from outside, I mean. Not if you were standing to one side, like I was.'

'So were you able to see the girl from there? Did you watch to see where she went eventually?'

'I could see her just fine. She had her bags with her by then, from off the bus. So I knew she was probably going to stay in Cooleyville after all. And I was curious about *where* she was going to stay. And then I remembered that Frank had said something about getting someone in to help when June hurt her leg — that's his wife, you know.' He glanced up at the judge, who nodded. 'Well, I got to thinking maybe she's the *one*, the one Frank was getting in to help Idy. So I was real curious then, and I waited to see what she'd do.'

'So if she was the girl Frank was getting in to help with June, you might think that someone from the house would come down and pick her up, wouldn't you.' Gail glanced around to see what reaction her words would cause.

Botts rose wearily to his feet. 'Speculation, Your Honor.'

'Overruled. Continue.' Fogg was as curious as the rest of them by now.

Jimmy cleared his throat again. 'I could tell she was getting nervous about there being nobody there to pick her up. The rest of the tourists all got back on the bus, and it left . . . going on to Duneville, I reckon. Anyway, I was almost about to go out there and introduce myself and see if I could help her when someone did come up. I was a bit surprised when I saw who it was, but not *too* surprised.' He paused for effect. The courtroom was hanging on his words.

'Not too surprised. Why was that, Jimmy? Why were you not surprised by the person who picked up the young woman at the bus stop?'

'Because it was something he might do. He didn't think I ever noticed, but I did. I saw how he looked at the girls, especially the pretty ones. He never saw me watching him, but I *did* watch him . . . all the time . . . once I figured out what he was doing.'

'And who was the person you saw? The one you watched all the time; the one who had such an interest in the young girls in town?'

'It was him.' Jimmy turned his gaze toward the defense table and the orange-clad prisoner seated there.

'I'm sorry, Buck. But you know it's true. I saw you, and I know you. *I know what was in your mind.'* He started to say something else but thought better of it and sank back with a sigh. It was hard work being a witness. Even harder when it felt like the whole world was watching you.

'Let the record show that the witness

has identified William Brandon as the person he saw picking up Sonia Mattingly at the bus stop in Cooleyville after her arrival there — as scheduled — on June 5th.'

'So ordered,' intoned Fogg. 'Do you have any further questions for this witness?'

'Only one, Your Honor.' Turning back to Jimmy, she smiled. 'We're almost done now, Jimmy. There's only one other thing we need to know. When Mr. Osterlitz and I discussed this matter with you at the sheriff's substation earlier, we showed you some photographs of women and asked you to pick out the one which most resembled the girl you saw at the bus stop. Do you remember that?'

'Yes, ma'am.'

'I'm going to show you the photograph you picked and I want to ask you now to confirm that it is indeed a picture of the woman you saw.' She moved to the witness stand and laid a small snapshot in front of him. 'Is this the girl you saw?'

'Yes, it is. She was a very pretty young woman. I wouldn't forget her face right away.'

Gail turned to Judge Fogg. 'You have a copy of the photograph Mr. Dunlap has just identified in front of you, Your Honor, along with photocopies of Sonia Mattingly's driver's license and her school employee I.D. from the Berkeley public school system. As you can see, there is little doubt it is the same woman.

'Mr. Botts?' She turned to the defense counsel. 'I've provided you with the same copies of the photographs. I think there is little doubt that the woman Jimmy saw getting off the bus in Cooleyville on June 5th, the same day she was scheduled to arrive there, was indeed Sonia Mattingly. And the only person who met her and took her someplace else was the defendant, William Brandon.' She turned back to Jimmy. 'Thank you, Jimmy. I have no further questions for you now.'

Jimmy stood and started to leave the witness box when a voice rang out.

'Just a moment.' It was Botts who had been conferring quietly with his client. 'I have a few questions for Mr. Dunlap.'

'Very well,' grumbled Fogg. 'But let's keep it brief, shall we?'

Botts looked down at some hastily scribbled notes for a moment then stepped forward. 'Now, Mr. Dunlap — or would you rather I call you Jimmy?' Jimmy shrugged and Botts went on. 'During your testimony you made a statement that you thought you 'knew what was going on in the defendant's mind,' didn't you?'

'Er . . . I don't recall saying that, exactly.' Jimmy looked uncomfortable, and ran a finger around his too-tight shirt collar.

'Well, I can repeat it to you if you like. You said, and I quote: 'I saw you, and I know you. *I know what was in your mind.*' Would you mind explaining to the court what you meant by that? How can you possibly 'know' what is in somebody else's mind?'

'Objection.' Gail rose. 'Counsel is badgering the witness. I think it was perfectly clear what Mr. Dunlap's intention was in his statement.'

'I'm not so sure, Counsel. I think I'll allow it. Let's see where this is going.' Fogg sighed. He had been right that it was going to be a long, difficult day.

'Mr. Dunlap?' Botts reiterated. 'What did you mean by such a statement?'

'Well, you see, sir, I have this guide . . . a spirit guide . . . who tells me things. White Feather. My Indian spirit guide. He's the one who warned me about Buck. Said he was just like me . . . except I got free of it all . . . back in San Francisco. I could have gone the same direction as Buck here, except I got caught . . . and *then* I got free.'

Gail closed her eyes and bent her head in frustration. All their hard work was about to be undone.

Connie reached over and took her hand. 'Wait a minute,' he whispered. 'This might not turn out as badly as we think.'

'When you say Mr. Brandon was 'just like you,' what do you mean by that, Mr. Dunlap?' Botts asked.

'He has the same bad seed in him that I had when I was young. I resented that nobody ever saw me for who I was. All they saw was my looks, and they laughed at me . . . all the time. Laughed and bullied me. And the girls? They never gave me the time of day. Got so I hated them all. Especially the pretty ones.

'When I got a little older, the only ones who would go with me, you know, let me have my way with them, were the ones I had to pay for. There were a lot of them like that in San Francisco, so I was all right with that . . . for a while. Then one night, after I had been with one of those 'for pay' girls a few times, I tried to talk to her a bit . . . tell her how pretty I thought she was.

'I asked her if she would go out with me on a regular basis, like a real girlfriend. But she just laughed at me. She laughed so long and so hard that she started to cry. I don't know . . . it got to me. Just went all over me, like a red cloud or something. And before I knew it, I had picked up a fireplace iron and hit her over the head with it. All the blood . . . it was something else. Something I've never forgotten to this day.'

'So you hit the young woman over the head. What happened to her? Did she survive the attack?'

'No. She died right then and there. I

didn't know what to do. I thought about running away, but I didn't think I'd get very far. They all knew me, those girls, and they knew I had been with her that night. I don't think I could have gotten away with it. So I just gave myself up. Didn't try to fight it at all. I was convicted of manslaughter and went away to prison . . . for a while. But then some doctors came in and gave me a bunch of tests. Then they took me to a hospital, somewhere . . . ' His voice wandered off.

'And what happened at this hospital, Mr. Dunlap? Do you recall?'

'Oh yes, I know what happened. They fixed my brain.'

'Fixed your brain?'

'Yes. They took me in to a room, all in white, and all the doctors and nurses were dressed in white too. And after a little bit they strapped me onto a table, and they put a little wooden paddle in my mouth, and then . . . but then I don't remember anything after that. I just know they told me they had shocked me . . . to fix my brain, you know.'

'Yes, I understand. So when you made

the statement about knowing what was in Mr. Brandon's mind — '

'Because my spirit guide told me that he is just like me — just like I was, before they fixed my brain. That's all I meant.'

'Yes, I see. You received shock treatment in a mental hospital, and now you believe you have a spirit guide who tells you things. Yes, I see completely.' Botts turned back to Judge Fogg. 'Thank you, Your Honor. I have no further questions for this witness.'

Gail got to her feet. 'Redirect, Your Honor?' He nodded. 'Jimmy, I have only one question for you. On June 5th, at the bus stop in Cooleyville, did you witness William 'Buck' Brandon meet the young woman later identified as Sonia Mattingly, and take her away with him in his car?'

'Yes, ma'am. That I did, most surely. And White Feather didn't have anything to do with that, either.' There was a brief outburst of muffled laughter quickly shushed by the judge's gavel.

'Thank you very much, Mr. Dunlap. You have done your community a great service today and we are all grateful for your honesty and your bravery in coming forward.'

Judge Fogg took only a short time to review all the evidence before making his pronouncement.

'It is the court's opinion that the evidence presented here today is more than sufficient to grant the district attorney's request for the arraignment of the defendant William Brandon for one count of murder in the first degree and a second count of attempted murder in the first degree. After examining our dockets, a time for trial will be set within ninety days. The accused is to be held, without bail, at the Grass Valley State Prison facility until then. Mr. Osterlitz?' He turned to the prosecutor's table. 'I expect you will wish to coordinate with the D.A.'s office and offer the same level of support at the trial as you have here for the arraignment?'

'Yes, Your Honor,' Connie responded. With the amount of evidence gathered thus far, and with the continuing efforts of the state authorities to unearth additional remains believed to be hidden in the collapsed mines in the area, the trial itself should go smoothly, now that the real burden of attaining arraignment had been met. 'We'll be glad to cooperate in any way that we can with the D.A.'s office.'

'Good. I must say how grateful our community should be to you and your team for their expertise in this matter. I expect many of our people will be relieved to know what really happened to their loved ones. You've provided a real service here today, and I for one thank you for it.' He nodded cordially to each of the before rising. 'That's all. Court is dismissed.'

★   ★   ★

'Well, there's several more difficult tasks we have to complete before we can get back home,' Connie said, stretching in relief as they left the justice court.

'I know.' Gail was exhausted. Her cross-examination of poor old Jimmy had taken its toll. Now she was trying to decide whether she should contact the adult protective services while they were still in the area. At least Frank's remaining 'strays' had a roof over their heads and food to eat. Now that the evil serpent that had been Buck Brandon was defanged, perhaps the Garden of Eden that was Cooleyville could flourish once more.

Frank wasn't such a bad person, really — just overwhelmed with all of his responsibilities. Maybe things would get better for the family, now that some of the ghosts had been laid to rest.

'First,' Connie said, 'I've made arrangements for us to have a final meeting with Nick and Marilee when we get back to San Francisco. I'm not looking forward to it, but she has to be told what you found.' He paused, searching for the right words. 'It should only be a matter of time,' he went on, 'before the remains you stumbled over in the Clarissa Mine can be matched up with Sonia Mattingly's DNA records. I think Marilee should be prepared not to keep up her hopes any further.'

Gail nodded. 'You're right. And,

181

Connie — I'd rather this case be *pro bono*. I really don't feel like making any profit off this particular expedition, no matter what it cost us . . . if that's all right with you.'

'It's your call. But in this instance I happen to agree with you. I'm just so thankful to get you back in one piece. From what Hugo tells me, we could just as easily have had an unhappier outcome. Speaking of which — we have to talk about the final chapter in this unhappy saga.'

'Idy.' Gail's voice broke. All this time, through all the terror in the mine, and the seemingly unending formality of Buck Brandon's arraignment trial, she had never lost sight of her ultimate goal: bringing the arsonist who caused Idy's death to justice. 'What proofs have we about the cause of the fire?'

Connie scratched his head and pulled out a lined yellow pad and a pen. 'Well, for starters, we've gotten sworn affidavits from all of the fire authorities on hand that night that a large concentration of accelerant was found just inside Idy's bedroom door. Not only that, but the windows in her room which opened out onto the veranda had been blocked with a board from the outside.'

'A board?'

'Yes. It was actually nailed right across the outside window frames. She never could have removed it from the inside by herself. She wouldn't have had the strength.'

'Did the authorities conduct any sort of investigation as to the source of the accelerant?'

'Yes.' Gail blew a stray lock from her forehead. 'I didn't realize it at the time, but Judge Cooley was moved by the incident after we talked about it, and he has been pushing ever since for a thorough investigation.'

'You mean after you spoke to him when you were staying there right after the fire?'

'We talked about it that very next morning. I tried to impress upon him that it was not right for the authorities to just 'sweep that mess under the carpet.' He is still resentful that they didn't do more to uncover what really happened when his

183

wife died a few years ago. Because of that, he has gotten involved in this matter, and I think he may be able to prevail — particularly in light of recent events.'

'Is there any way we can link Buck to the fire?'

'Hugo noticed some suspicious-looking cans sitting near the work area at the Clarissa the day I was trapped there. He brought them to the attention of the authorities and the contents are being tested at the state facility in Grass Valley. We should know for sure in a few days, but I think there's very little doubt about it.'

'And the board across the windows? Where did that come from? Do we know yet?'

'Well, that's the most interesting part. It looks as though that particular piece of lumber is a close match to the lumber used to shore up the mine entrance at the Clarissa.' She paused to reflect. 'They'll have to finish uncovering the main entrance of course. But once they do they'll be able to compare that lumber with the board across Idy's windows. If all that checks out as expected, I think we can add an indictment for Idy's murder to Buck's charges by the time he actually comes up for trial. At least that would be my hope.'

'What I'm still wondering,' Connie said, 'is why he should have killed that innocent girl. Any ideas, Gail?'

'The poor kid had a fixation on him. I remember that when I first met him over a meal at Frank's place, I couldn't help but notice how Idy hung on every word Buck uttered. I remember wondering just how long she'd been pining after him.'

'And?' Connie prompted.

'Idy sat herself next to him and began talking to him about something. She was whispering, so I couldn't hear what she was saying, but at one point he shook his head angrily, and then seemed to ignore her entirely for the rest of the meal.'

Connie frowned thoughtfully. 'If Idy had a crush on Buck, she'd have been watching his movements pretty closely. She might have suspected him of the earlier disappearance of a girl she'd been jealous of, and was pressing him for a date as a price for keeping quiet.'

'So he had to shut her up? I'm not sure Idy would be that devious . . . she was a simple soul. I guess we may never know for sure unless the police can get a confession from him.'

Connie smiled and patted her hand. 'So all's well that ends well?'

'One would hope,' Gail said with a sigh. 'One would hope.'

THE END